gre

# SPIDERS

. . . . . . . . . . . . . . . . . . . . . . . . . . . . . . . . . . . . . . .

## OF AUSTRALIA

Terence Lindsey

Series Editor: Louise Egerton

NEW
HOLLAND

Published in Australia by
New Holland Publishers (Australia) Pty Ltd
Sydney • Auckland • London • Cape Town

14 Aquatic Drive Frenchs Forest NSW 2086 Australia
218 Lake Road Northcote Auckland New Zealand
86 Edgware Rd London W2 2EA United Kingdom
80 McKenzie Street Cape Town 8001 South Africa

First published in 1998 by New Holland Publishers (Australia) Pty Ltd.
Reprinted in 1999, 2001, 2002, 2004, 2005, 2006

National Library of Australia Cataloguing-in-Publication Data:

Lindsey, Terence, 1941–.
Spiders of Australia
Includes index

ISBN 1 86436 332 0

1. Spiders—Australia 2. Spiders—Australia—Identification.
I. Title. (Series: Green guide (New Holland)).

595.40994

Project Manager: Fiona Doig
Series Editor: Louise Egerton
Design and Illustrations: Laurence Lemmon-Warde
Cover Design: Peta Nugent
Picture Researcher: Bronwyn Rennex
Reproduction: DNL Resources
Printed and bound by Everbest Printing Co. Ltd (China)

### Photographic Acknowledgments
**Abbreviations:** NHIL = New Holland Image Library; LT = Lochman Transparencies.
**Photograph positions:** t = top; b = bottom; c = centre; m = main; i = inset; l = left; r = right, fc = front cover; bc = back cover.
**Robert Brunet:** p. 9t, 11i, 14, 18b, 19t, 20, 22t, 38, 42, 50–51, 53, 55t, 60, 64b, 65, 66m & i, 68m, 83b, 84, 86b, 87b, 90m & i, 94b; **Densey Clyne/Mantis Wildlife:** p. 26, 30, 35t, 61, 70, 89, bc b; **Jim Frazier/Mantis Wildlife:** p. 71; **Pavel German:** p. 6t, 7t, 12b, 21b, 27, 33i, 39, 52b, 59, 62–63, 73, 81, 82b, 91, 94t; **Mike Gray/Nature Focus:** p. 35b, 43, 47, 63i, 72; **Wade Hughes/LT:** p. 7b, 25t, 28–29, 69, 78m & i; **John Kleczkowski/LT:** fc c, p. 18t, 34t, 41b, 56b, 68i, 74–75; **D. Knowles/LT:** fc cr, p. 4, 5, 8, 9b, 10–11, 15, 16b, 17b, 21t, 24b, 25b, 32m, 33m, 40, 44b, 45, 46, 48m & i, 49t&b, 51i, 54, 55i, 57, 64t, 75i, 77, 79m&i, 83t, 85, 88, 93, 95, bc t; **Jiri Lochman/LT:** fc t&b, p. 3, 6b, 13t, 16t, 17t, 19b, 29i, 31, 36t&b, 37, 41t, 44t, 56t, 67, 82t, 86t; **Peter Marsack/LT:** front flap, 12t, 13b, 22b, 24t, 32; **G. Saueracher/LT:** 52t, 58; **Dennis Sarson/LT:** 23t&b, 34b, 80, 92; **T. Tucker:** back flap.

# CONTENTS

# An Introduction to Spiders

*❈*

*T*his book is a preliminary guide to the spiders of Australia. It is intended as an introduction to their habits and to those Australian groups that are especially common, interesting or significant to humans.

Scientific and technical terms have been kept to a minimum, although some are unavoidable because many of the structures of spiders have no equivalents among familiar animals. A spider's chelicerae, for example, may be thought of as loosely equivalent to its jaws or fangs, yet they lie entirely outside the animal's mouth and are really neither.

Australian spiders have been grouped here into behavioural categories rather than by relationship. Many spider groups that are not related, however, behave in comparable ways. Conversely, many closely related species may have very different lifestyles. For these reasons members of the same family may crop up in different sections of this book.

## Different Kinds of Spiders

The popular concept that spiders are either large hairy ground-dwellers that come out at night or large not-so-hairy things that sit in the middle of large silken webs, often during the day, is basically sound.

Many of Australia's spiders are indeed large and hairy. They live in burrows in the ground and are technically known as the mygalomorphs. These were the earliest spiders and they are sometimes referred to as the 'ancient' or 'primitive' spiders. Mygalomorphs have two pairs of book-lungs with which to breathe and chelicerae that strike downwards like pick-axes.

*Almost all of the 'ancient' spiders live on the ground.*

The second group, the araneomorphs, are called here the 'modern' spiders. Modern spiders have only one pair of book-lungs but they have in addition an entirely separate breathing system involving a network of tiny tubes that carry oxygen directly to all parts of the body. They have fangs that are held horizontally and move inward like a pair of pincers. Many modern spiders use silk to snare their prey.

## Lifestyles of the Modern Spiders

The modern spiders span a wide range of lifestyles but they can be grouped into four categories according to their hunting behaviour. Like wolves, some spiders roam about, stalking their prey; in this book these are known as the 'roving spiders'. Others hunt more as cats do, hiding patiently in ambush; these are the so-called 'sit-and-wait spiders'. Some spiders do not weave webs but

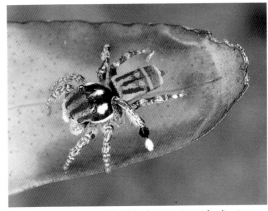

*Many of the 'modern' spiders, like this jumping spider, live in vegetation above the ground.*

nevertheless use silk to trap their prey, sometimes in ingenious ways. The spiders belonging to this category are characterised here as the 'snare-makers'. And lastly, there are those spiders that build the truly wheel-shaped webs we are familiar with in gardens; these are fittingly called the 'web-weavers'. The crucial feature of these webs is that they are designed to catch flying insects rather than crawling ones.

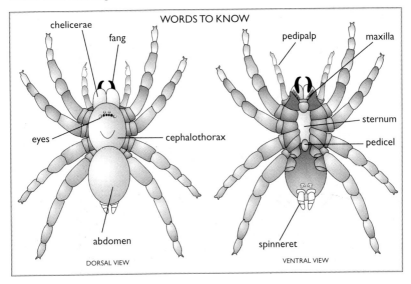

WORDS TO KNOW

chelicerae
fang
eyes
cephalothorax
abdomen
DORSAL VIEW

pedipalp
maxilla
sternum
pedicel
spinneret
VENTRAL VIEW

# What are the Main Characteristics of a Spider?

*Spiders are the most numerous and widespread of eight-legged animals. Others include scorpions, ticks and mites.*

Spiders, unlike insects, have eight legs; so do scorpions, ticks, mites and harvestmen but they are different in the following ways. Scorpions have a pair of crab- or lobster-like nippers, an obvious sting at the end of their long flexible tails and bodies divided into many segments. Harvestmen, which are quite easily confused with daddy-long-legs spiders but are not spiders, have only two eyes. Ticks have minute heads and enormous abdomens and most mites are too small to even count the legs without a microscope.

**FOUR EYES OR MORE**
The basic spider specification calls for eight eyes but in many species the central pair are much reduced or absent and a few species have only four eyes.

# Where do Spiders Live?

Spiders live almost everywhere. There are spiders that live in houses, others that live in deserts, there are rainforest spiders and spiders of the marshes; some spiders even live along the coast, their shelters becoming underwater caverns when the tide comes in.

Minute species hunt in the grass, others lie in wait for prey in flowers, some hide under rocks or beneath the bark of trees and still others seldom emerge from their burrows in the ground. There are undercover lurkers and those capable of building webs several metres in diameter; at their hub they wait motionless for all the world to see.

Many spiders are active during the day but an equally numerous contingent emerges when the sun goes down. Spiders are extremely abundant and usually too numerous to count but several studies suggest that on a single hectare of ordinary grassland or woodland there may be in excess of one million individual spiders.

*Wolf spiders live in holes in the ground.*

# The Body Parts of a Spider

*T*he body of a spider has two main parts or segments: the cephalothorax, which might be viewed as a sort of head and chest combined, and the abdomen. The two are joined by a narrow waist called the pedicel. The abdomen contains organs for breathing, food storage, silk production and reproduction. The cephalothorax contains the brain, poison glands and the sucking stomach.

*One conspicuous way in which spiders differ from insects is in having two main body segments instead of three.*

   Externally, the cephalothorax bears six pairs of appendages: the chelicerae, the pedipalps and four pairs of jointed legs. Its upper surface is armoured and called the carapace, and there are one or more rows of forward-facing eyes.

## Jaws Spider Style

The chelicerae might well be thought of as fangs or jaws except that they lie entirely outside the mouth and their mechanism is very much more intricate. Nevertheless, their function is approximately equivalent to jaws — they bite, handle and crush food. At their tip they carry the hollow fangs, connected to poison glands in the cephalothorax that inject venom into the victim's body.

## Mouth Tools

Commonly abbreviated to palps, the pedipalps are jointed, complicated organs situated close to the mouth that might be thought of as a sort of toolbelt. They function to some extent as accessory limbs but they also carry various devices to assist in touching, feeding, grooming and several other routine functions. In males they are specially modified for the transference of sperm to the female's genital opening.

*Looking rather like abbreviated legs, the palps show clearly in this portrait of a trampoline spider.*

# How do Spiders Breathe?

*A* spider's breathing organs are on the underside of the abdomen and there are two distinct types. Ancient or primitive spiders use a distinctive organ known as a book-lung, which works a little like the gills of a fish but in air rather than water. This organ is essentially a hollow pouch containing many sheets of tissue arranged rather like the pages of a book — or perhaps even more like the floors of a tiny multi-storey carpark — through which air circulates.

Ancient spiders have two pairs of book-lungs, modern spiders only one pair. However, modern spiders have an additional breathing system that closely resembles that used by insects. Openings in the body wall, called spiracles, lead to a system of fine tubes running through the body and these tubes, or 'tracheae', deliver oxygen directly to muscles and tissues. The spiracle can be opened or shut, a refinement that has far-reaching implications for a spider's lifestyle because it conserves moisture. Primitive spiders can live only in burrows in the soil, which are areas of high humidity, but modern spiders can survive in the drier conditions that prevail above ground.

*The relatively inefficient book-lungs of the ancient spiders mostly confine them to a life on the ground.*

# Do Spiders have Hearts?

*T*hey do have hearts and also a simple circulatory system. The blood functions, as in humans and other animals, as a medium to carry oxygen, nutrients and other vital substances to the tissues, and to carry off carbon dioxide and other waste products.

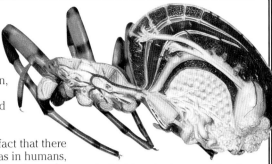

*A spider's heart is a boomerang-shaped organ in the upper part of the abdomen.*

The difference lies in the fact that there is no network of capillaries as in humans, so the blood merely pours from the ends of arteries into muscles and other tissues, collecting in large spaces of the body and finding its way back to the heart. There are valves at various points to maintain a one-way flow. Because there is no capillary system there is also only a primitive clotting mechanism and a spider with a puncture in its body wall may quickly bleed to death.

# A Spider's Stomach

*A* spider's digestive organs are strongly modified for its way of life. The most distinctive feature is the 'sucking' stomach, which functions — from a mechanical perspective — not entirely unlike a human lung. The stomach can be expanded, which exerts suction to bring food in from the mouth, and squeezed, which forces stomach contents backwards into the midgut. Solid particles are filtered out by hairs around the mouth and around the jaws.

*Spiders have powerful, muscular stomachs that function rather like bellows to suck liquid food in from the mouth.*

Several features enable the spider to deal with large quantities of food at a time. In particular, ducts from the stomach lead out into the limbs and ramify throughout much of the abdomen; in such areas the food gradually becomes absorbed by the tissues. By distributing the food in this way, spiders can eat a great deal more than their current requirements and can therefore go without further food for considerable periods of time.

# ANCIENT SPIDERS

# Who are the Ancient Spiders?

*The Tree Funnel-web is an exception to the general rule that ancient spiders live mostly on the ground.*

*T*here are major differences in the anatomy of spiders and these separate them into two distinct groups, with a few species clustered on the dividing line between the two. These two groups are usually called the ancient or primitive spiders and the modern spiders. Scientifically they are known as the mygalomorphs and araneomorphs respectively.

Australia has about 240 species of ancient spiders, divided among 10 families that are similar in general appearance and lifestyle. Ancient spiders are large and hairy, active mainly at night and live mostly in burrows in the ground by day. They include the well-known trapdoor spiders, the funnel-webs and the mouse spiders. They can usually be recognised by their very large chelicerae or 'fangs', which point forwards and move up and down instead of having pincerlike chelicerae that move from side to side as in modern spiders.

## How do Spiders Eat?

*Spiders use their stomachs like bellows to suck their victims dry.*

*S*piders have minute mouths. All chewing, and even digestion, goes on outside the spider's body. The chelicerae crush the spider's victim and inject its body with digestive enzymes. The result is a sort of 'soup' that the spider sucks up like drinking a milkshake through a straw, except that the sucking action comes not from the mouth but from the bellows-like stomach.

# How do Spiders Grab their Victims?

*F*or a ground-dwelling spider, fangs that strike downwards work very well because the ground provides a firm surface against which to impale a victim — in one funnel-web bite on record the spider's fangs penetrated the patient's fingernail. However for a spider attempting to dispatch its prey on a more yielding surface, such as a web, downward-striking fangs are hopelessly impractical.

A spider's orb-web is a supremely effective device for catching flying insects but before they could 'invent' the orb-web primitive spiders had to do something about their fangs. Essentially, the solution

*Spiders use their chelicerae (or 'fangs') to snatch and hold their victims while their venom and digestive enzymes do their work.*

that emerged involved swivelling them 90 degrees inwards so that they would open and shut from the sides. The mechanical difference between a pick-axe and a pair of pincers conveys the basic idea.

*Jumping spiders differ from many other spiders in not wrapping their prey in silk before dining.*

# Trapdoor Spiders

*Most of the many kinds of trapdoor spiders are shades of brown or black in colour.*

There are several different families of trapdoor spiders. All members of this group live in burrows and in many species the openings to their burrows are fitted with a hinged lid. There are however such things as trapdoor spiders that do not seal their burrows with a 'trapdoor' and there is at least one species that does not even live on the ground but builds an artificial 'burrow' high in a rainforest tree.

A typical trapdoor spider is big, hairy, solidly built, generally brown or brownish and it often has a pattern of markings, either pale or dark, on its body. Usually highly camouflaged, they are very difficult to locate. Large species are about 3 cm in body length but many others are much smaller. They occur in almost all habitats across Australia, including the eastern forests and the deserts of the interior.

## Defence and Attack

Their lifestyle is sluggish and sedentary. Despite their formidable appearance, trapdoor spiders are timid and will usually try to run away if molested. If they cannot escape they may cower motionless, with their legs huddled close against their body. Their bite is not considered dangerous.

**A LIGHTNING BITE**

In laboratory studies under controlled conditions, the speed of an American trapdoor spider's leap from its burrow onto its victim was once carefully measured: from launch to grab took exactly 0.03 seconds.

Trapdoor spiders are active at night, when most open their trapdoors just a crack and lurk in the opening. When an unwary cricket, beetle or some similar small animal happens to walk by within range, the spider leaps out with astonishing speed, seizes its victim and hauls it back into its burrow to be eaten at leisure.

# Mouse Spiders

*Mouse spiders look very like trapdoor spiders except for their very large chelicerae.*

Most mouse spiders could easily be mistaken for trapdoor spiders except for their relatively enormous chelicerae. However, one of the most obvious species is the Red-headed Mouse Spider, in which the sexes are so different from one another that for years they were regarded as entirely distinct species. While the female is squat, black and shiny, the male has a deep blue abdomen and a bright red head. Males are about 1.5 cm in length; females about 2 cm. Although absent from Tasmania, the Red-headed Mouse Spider is widespread across mainland Australia.

Among members of the mouse spider group, females are usually timid but males can be aggressive to humans. Their bite is not known to be fatal to humans but life-threatening effects have been reported and ordinary prudence suggests that males, in particular, should be regarded as dangerous.

## Underground Lifestyle

Like trapdoor spiders, mouse spiders live in burrows in the ground, often along the banks of rivers or streams. Their burrows may extend to a depth of one metre or more, although those belonging to males are very much shallower than those of females. Females live almost entirely underground but males can occasionally be found wandering about in broad daylight, especially after rain, in search of a mate.

Courting males visit females in their burrows where they are often killed and eaten after mating. The female lays about 60 eggs, which she wraps in a cocoon of silk and installs in a sealed, specially excavated side-burrow midway down her own. The spiderlings remain with her for some time after hatching.

# What Burrows do Trapdoor Spiders Build?

*T*he burrows built by trapdoor spiders come in all shapes and sizes. They may be shallow or up to a metre deep. While some are vertical, others are inclined and they may be straight or winding. Some trapdoor spiders build forked burrows and many build a chamber off to the side of their burrows as a sort of bolthole in which to hide should a predator come calling or as a sort of airlock

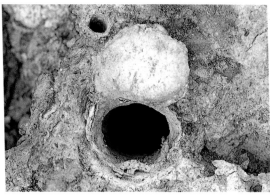

*A typical trapdoor spider burrow can be sealed with a hinged lid or 'trapdoor'.*

in which to seal themselves if the ground above should be flooded.

The trapdoors themselves vary, too, according to species, almost to the extent that a specialist can identify an occupant from the form of its door. Some species build simple hinged lids, while others construct elaborate, stout, carefully camouflaged covers with bevelled rims that fit snugly into the burrow's entrance.

# How to Build a Burrow in Loose Sand

*The narrow, slit-like burrow entrances of slit spiders helps protect their owners from predators.*

*S*ome spiders build ingeniously designed burrows to suit their special circumstances. Loose sand, for example, makes burrow construction extremely difficult but the slit spiders of the Simpson Desert sand dunes have evolved a solution. They excavate a narrow, slit-shaped burrow at a shallow angle on the slope of a sand dune where the encrusting effect of wind and sun on the sand is at its greatest. Being slit-shaped, the narrow entrance also obstructs the entry of predators such as skinks and geckos.

# How do Spiders See?

*O*n the whole, not very well. Spiders are hunters that have brought the sense of touch to a pinnacle of hi-tech development. Sight is very much secondary in much the same way that smell is largely secondary to sight in humans. Vision is often reserved for close-up work and every line of evidence, from anatomy, appearance

*Some spiders, like this huntsman, have eyes arranged in two parallel rows.*

and behaviour, indicates that many spiders cannot form images of objects that are more than a few centimetres away. Exceptions include many spiders of the 'roving hunters' groups, and especially the jumping spiders. These spiders have relatively enormous eyes that are capable of seeing several metres.

## Are Spiders' Eyes like Those of Insects?

*T*he structure of a spider's eye is very different to that of a bird's or mammal's, even though they have several features common to both types. Nor are they like the eyes of insects. A spider's eyes are 'simple', unlike the multi-faceted 'compound' eyes of flies and other insects, and they are technically called 'ocelli'.

As with human eyes, they have a lens and a retina, and in many cases a tapetum, which is the same mirror-like structure inside the eye that causes a cat's eyes to shine at night. The basic spider specification calls for eight eyes but in some groups the central pair is degenerate or lacking and these have only six; a few have only four.

*Jumping spiders are notable for their exceptionally well-developed eyes.*

**OGLING ONE ANOTHER**
To witness the seeing abilities of a jumping spider, watch it; it will very likely ogle you right back. It will turn to face you and swivel its body to follow your finger as you wave it about.

# What do Spiders do when it Rains?

*Many web-weavers like this garden spider merely drip-dry in the rain.*

*H*eavy rain makes life difficult for small creatures living in burrows and the same is true of the slow 'sheet-flooding' so characteristic of much of Australia's flat desert interior after rain but spiders have evolved several devices for coping with both.

One of the commonest devices used by some trapdoor spiders in their burrows is a dead-end chamber. This they construct midway down their burrow but inclined upwards and off to one side. During floods the burrow fills with water but a large bubble of air is trapped in the silk-lined chamber. Here the spider can survive for considerable periods while the flood recedes.

> **SNUG PLUGS**
> The Pebble Spider stoppers its burrow entrance with a pebble, silk-rimmed to fit snugly. Many trapdoor spiders waterproof their burrows with a snug-fitting trapdoor.

## Dealing with Floods

*M*any wolf spiders in the arid interior of Australia use a slightly different technique to protect themselves from being flooded out. The basic idea is the same as using sandbags to build levees around a low-lying town. As they build their burrows, many species take the earth removed from the tunnel and simply heap it around the entrance to form a levee.

Other species go further: one uncommon species of wolf

*Wolf spiders often 'waterproof' their underground dens with a dyke or levee of soil, pebbles or twigs.*

spider, aptly named the Shuttlecock Spider, collects twigs and binds them with silk to form a palisade around the entrance to its burrow. These barriers may be about 8 cm high and from a distance they look a little like badminton shuttlecocks half buried in the sandy soil.

# Can Spiders Swim?

*L*ike any other air-breathing animal, spiders drown in water but there are many species equipped with built-in scuba-diving equipment. The nursery-web or fishing spiders, for example, are common around the margins of pools and streams. One may spend long periods resting patiently at the waterside with its hindlegs on the bank but the front pair extended and resting quietly on the water surface. It waits for the merest ripple of an unwary small fish or similar aquatic creature, then pounces on it.

*The nursery-web spider is unusual among spiders in its agility in water — it can run about on the surface and even dive.*

It can run about on the surface of calm water easily and even plunges below the surface in its pursuit of prey. The tangle of tiny hairs on its body resist wetting and trap a layer of air between it and the water. This air bubble enables the spider to breathe for some minutes. The same principle enables many other hairy spiders, such as trapdoor spiders, to survive for some time immersed in water.

# Life in a Bubble of Silk

*The Water Spider of Europe is the world's only truly aquatic spider.*

*O*ne non-Australian species, the Water Spider of Europe, goes further and spends its entire life beneath the surface. It constructs a web of silk anchored to waterplants and woven so closely that not even water particles can penetrate it. About the size and shape of a thimble, the web bellies upward and trapped within it is a large bubble of air in which the spider lives. Periodically the spider visits the surface to replenish its air supply.

# Funnel-web Spiders

*Most of the 30-odd species of funnel-webs cannot be specifically identified on casual examination.*

The name 'funnel-web' refers to the spider's home but it is somewhat misleading in that the 'funnel' is really shaped more like a sort of sock of woven silk, with a chamber at the 'toe' in which the spider rests during the day. At night it emerges to hunt. The shelter is constructed in a cavity of almost any sort — under a log, for example, or in a rock crevice. Very occasionally, a funnel-web excavates its own burrow in loose soil into which it weaves its 'sock'. In this particular respect the funnel-web differs little from other spiders that burrow but one detail to note that is reasonably reliable is whether the silk lining stops at the entrance or extends noticeably outside or beyond it. If the latter, then there is a good chance that the occupant is a funnel-web.

## Appearance and Distribution

There are at least 30 species of funnel-web spiders but they all look very much the same and identification to species level is difficult. Males are about 2.5 cm long; females about 3.5 cm. In most the carapace is a glossy blue–black in colour but this varies slightly with species, season, sex and state of moulting. The abdomen is covered in fine hairs with an effect like soft velvet. All funnel-webs have very large chelicerae and two spinnerets extend as spikes backwards from the tip of the abdomen.

Strongly associated with the Great Dividing Range and adjacent slopes and coastal forests, the distribution of funnel-webs extends from northeastern Queensland southwards at least to the Malacoota region of eastern Victoria.

## Sydney Funnel-web Spider

*The deadly Sydney Funnel-web's aggressive stance serves as a warning that it is about to attack.*

The Sydney Funnel-web is notorious as one of the deadliest of all spiders to humans — although it is probably unsafe to regard any other funnel-web species as any less so. Not so long ago, many bites resulted in a fatality. Recent years have seen the development of antivenenes so effective that full recovery is usually speedy and uneventful but even so a bite from a funnel-web should be dealt with as a grave emergency.

Confrontations with humans seem especially common in sandstone areas but Sydney Funnel-webs are not confined to such areas. They often occur in gardens and males, in particular, sometimes enter houses. This often happens when males are searching for females but it can also happen after long periods of heavy rain when presumably many are flooded out of their burrows. Occasionally they crawl into shoes or clothing left lying on the floor.

*The Sydney Funnel-web is the deadliest of all spiders and is often encountered in that city's suburbs.*

21

# Are Spiders Dangerous?

*The Red-headed Mouse-spider — so called from the male's bright colours — ranks high on the list of dangerous spiders.*

*T*he quick answer is yes, sometimes very dangerous indeed — but only a few.

Although almost all spiders have poison fangs, very few are life-threatening to humans. To begin with, the vast majority of species are so small that their fangs cannot penetrate human skin, so they cannot inject venom. Many — if not most — are timid and hard to provoke into biting. In most cases a spider's venom is too feeble or it may be delivered in too small a quantity to pose any serious threat to humans, although the bite may be extremely painful and produce severe local swelling.

*The Tree Funnel-web is unusual among funnel-webs in building its lair high on the trunks of trees.*

## The Dangerous Ones

Of course there are exceptions and a few spiders should be regarded as very dangerous indeed. The Sydney Funnel-web, in particular, is sometimes quite aggressive, willing to bite a human under very little provocation and its venom is deadly. Fatalities from their bites were common before the advent of modern antivenenes. These are very effective and fatalities are now rare, provided medical care is promptly provided.

Other spiders known to be extremely dangerous include — in approximate order of menace — any other funnel-webs; red-back spiders; mouse spiders, especially the Red-headed Mouse Spider; fiddle-back spiders; dysderid spiders; big-jawed sac spiders and brown badge spiders. These are the ones known to cause, at least in some cases, severe illness or, very rarely, even death in humans but others may also be harmful.

### DISEASE-CARRYING VENOM

Although the venom of the White-tailed Spider is not deadly, it carries bacteria which may cause dangerous side effects for some people. The bacteria usually result in a necrotic condition around the bite that can sometimes be extremely difficult to treat successfully.

# How Common are Dangerous Spiders?

*F*or bushwalkers, confrontation with a dangerous spider is unlikely, except perhaps when gathering wood for a campfire or some similar activity. On the other hand, in and around the home there are several spiders capable of delivering a dangerous bite, with or without provocation. Prevention is very much better than cure. Do not mess with a large spider. Always wear good heavy-duty gardening gloves and gaiters when working in the garden or for any other task involving garden litter and similar trash in and around the home.

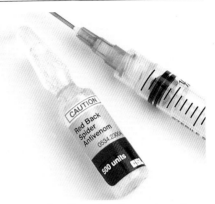

*Antivenes such as this one have done much to reduce fatalities from spider bites in recent years.*

## WHAT TO DO WHEN A DANGEROUS SPIDER BITES

- Do not panic. Get the victim calm, comfortable, warm and lying down as quickly as possible.
- If you have a good, up-to-date first-aid manual handy, follow the instructions in that book.
- Do not do anything to the bite.
- Do not elevate the bitten area.
- Do not give the patient anything to drink.
- If the bite is on a limb and is definitely from a funnel-web — but not other-wise — apply a pressure bandage (as for a sprain) to the entire limb. Immobilise it with a splint.
- Seek medical help immediately or drive the patient promptly to the casualty department of the nearest hospital. If you can safely take the spider along as well, then so much the better.

*The infamous Red-back is probably second only to the Sydney Funnel-web in deadliness but fatalities are now very rare.*

# Why is Funnel-web Venom So Toxic?

*To be useful to a spider, its venom must be effective on a wide range of different animals. In the case of the funnel-web, this spectrum just happens to include humans.*

*F*rom the spider's perspective, the whole point of an attack on prey using venom is to subdue the victim as quickly as possible without risking injury to itself. There is of course no biological advantage to the spider in going to the trouble of manufacturing venom deadly to an animal thousands of times bigger than itself. So why is it that funnel-web venom kills humans? It seems a reasonable question, especially since the same poison seems to affect cats and dogs only mildly, but there is no simple answer.

Funnel-web venom is in fact a very complex chemical cocktail incorporating a wide range of virulent components, which is why it took decades of research to arrive at an effective antivenene. Animals vary widely in their susceptibility to poison; to be useful a funnel-web's venom needs to be effective and quick-acting against a wide range of victims. It seems predators that rely on venom are compelled to take the 'shotgun' approach rather than targeting just one particular species of prey but the broader the spectrum, the greater the chance that some other animal will also be accidentally targeted. So it would seem that, in the case of funnel-webs, humans are just caught in the cross-fire of this intricate chemical conflict between predator and prey.

# Which is a Spider's Most Sensitive Organ?

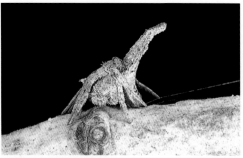

*Spiders use silk partly as an extension of their sense of touch.*

*M*uch of the natural history of spiders can be summed up in a single notion: the sense of touch. Just as birds rely heavily on sight and many mammals on smell, spiders have an extremely sophisticated sense of touch. Humans locate sounds in space mainly by subconsciously assessing the minute difference in pitch and volume

*Each of this trampoline spider's long outstretched legs bears a sensitive vibration sensor at its tip.*

reaching one ear compared to that reaching the other ear. Spiders use much the same 'stereo' method but applied to touch. They have extremely sensitive touch sensors in their feet and these they use to sense minute vibrations.

Long legs are more effective than short legs in this respect because spreading the delicate foot sensors farther apart enhances the stereo effect. In addition, analysing data from eight such sensors instead of two — as in human ears — boosts precision. Even the spider's web itself — with the spider perched at its centre, each sensitive foot upon a delicate thread that extends beyond the reach of the animal itself — can be viewed as a device for extending the spider's sensory scope.

# Can Spiders Taste?

As well as organs of touch, spiders also have highly sensitive organs of taste on their feet and at the tips of their pedipalps. The receptors consist of specially modified hollowed hairs. Spiders also have elaborate sensory systems for analysing air currents, stresses on their skin and the relative position of their legs, as well as, perhaps, conventional senses of smell and hearing.

### THE POWER OF SCENT
It is possible to attract male funnel-web spiders to a trap baited with a captive female. Such a trap often works successfully even if the female is removed, so that her scent is the only possible lingering sign of her former presence. Males may even initiate courtship behaviour at such a trap, which suggests that receptive females release scent as part of their mating behaviour.

*This wolf spider has both taste and touch sensors on its feet.*

# Is it Useful to be Hairy?

*Brush-footed spiders live in long burrows on riverbanks and their hairy bodies help them to avoid drowning when water levels rise.*

*T*he brush-footed spiders are hairy all over and dull reddish brown or greyish brown in colour. These spiders live a seemingly precarious existence along the banks of rivers and creeks in burrows that are sometimes winding. However they have developed some ingenious methods of living a life that is threatened by rising water levels.

Like the trapdoor spiders, some of these spiders build a door to their burrow entrance that they seal when waters rise. They remain inside the chamber, living off the air trapped inside. Some species also build a tiny, silk-lined side chamber into their burrows within which they remain when the main shaft floods.

Regardless of the type of burrow, for all spiders in this group hairiness becomes an advantage during floods as the fine hairs around the spider's body trap air, which the spider breathes when its burrow becomes flooded. Such an air supply can often last a long period of time — enough for the spider to survive the flood.

# Do Spiders Utter Sounds?

*S*everal species of spiders can produce sounds. In Australia the most notable of these are the barking or whistling spiders.

These spiders are equipped with a row of stiff, flattened spines along the base of their pedipalps and a similar row of spines along their chelicerae or jaws. By vigorously rubbing the two rows together, these spiders are able to produce a thin whistling note: this method of producing sound is called stridulation. These spiders stridulate during both hunting and courtship but the reason for this is unknown.

# Can Spiders Climb Smooth Vertical Surfaces?

$S$ome cannot and the spider that occasionally turns up in your bathtub has fallen in and is probably permanently trapped because its feet cannot get a grip on the smooth, steep porcelain surface. However, many spiders can scale vertical surfaces with ease, including some surprisingly large ones, such as the brush-footed spiders.

These spiders strongly resemble other ancient spiders except that most are not quite so big — up to about 3.5 cm in body length. The other feature that sets them apart is the tuft of tiny hairs that they bear at the tip of each foot. Under the microscope these are revealed as stiff and minutely hooked and spiked. It is these that give the spider the ability to nimbly clamber up smooth vertical surfaces.

Brush-footed spiders are common in various habitats across Australia west of the Great Dividing Range. Like other primitive spiders, they live in burrows in the ground, from which they emerge at night to hunt. Not much is known of the effects of their venom but at least one species in Western Australia is strongly suspected of having a potentially lethal bite. These spiders can be extremely aggressive if provoked and are best left alone.

> **TITAN OF SPIDERS**
> One group of the barking and whistling spiders includes the enormous bird-eating spiders. These are the largest of all spiders: one Australian member is about 6 cm in body length; its legs span about 16 cm — wider than a page in this book. Its fangs alone measure 1 cm in length.

*The brush-footed spiders are able to climb smooth as well as rough surfaces with ease. Some species, called the barking spiders, rub their palps and chelicerae together to produce a 'barking' sound.*

ROVING HUNTERS

# Who are the Oddballs of the Spider World?

*Despite their anatomical differences, the 'living-link' spiders resemble wolf spiders very strongly in appearance.*

There are a few spiders that do not fit into the category of either ancient or modern spiders, and several of these occur in Australia. Technically they are called the hypochilomorphs and they combine the features of both ancient and modern spiders in having pincer-type jaws like modern spiders but two pairs of book-lungs like ancient ones. Two small families alone represent this 'living link' group of spiders in Australia, both of which have members that live entirely in caves.

## Which Spiders Inhabit Caves?

One species of cave-dwelling spider, the Tasmanian Cave Spider, belongs to that curious category of spiders that display both modern and ancient anatomical features. It has remarkably long, slender legs spanning about 18 cm.

Its body is rich red and deep black in colour, with yellow book-lungs. Although found only in caves, the Tasmanian Cave Spider has eyes and can apparently use them — an unusual feature among cave-dwelling animals. It builds a horizontal sheet web with which to catch its prey.

Several other species live in caves: the Carrai Cave Spider, for example, is confined to the tiny cave of that name in eastern New South Wales. These spiders intrigue zoologists because they are considered very ancient, yet they catch their prey with the aid of simplified silk webs, a strategy thought to be relatively modern. All other known species are confined to ancient beech forests in the southeast but little is known of their habits.

**ROVERS' ANCESTRY**
The roving hunters are modern spiders. They have breathing equipment that enables them to live comfortably above ground, unlike the ancient spiders. Although these spiders are ground-dwellers, spider experts now believe that most roving hunters are descended from web-weaving ancestors.

# Paragons of Motherhood

*A*lthough attentive mothers by comparison to many invertebrates, few spiders lavish as much care on their offspring as those roving hunters, the wolf spiders. Even before her eggs hatch, a mother wolf spider takes great care of her egg-sac, carrying it everywhere she goes. At the entrance to her burrow she may even 'incubate' it by exposing it to sunlight, periodically rotating it to maintain an even temperature.

When the eggs hatch, several hundred tiny spiderlings climb up the mother's legs and onto her body where special knobbed and minutely hooked hairs tangle. Onto these, the spiderlings, with their safety-lines to provide secure anchorage, cling like city commuters in a subway train. Other spiders carry their young for a few days but wolf spiders guard and carry theirs for many weeks. Her patience is not infinite, however, for if some stray among her eyes she will brush them roughly aside with her front legs, knocking many of them off her body altogether.

> ## CAUGHT IN THE LIGHT
> Wolf spiders are extremely common and easily found with a flashlight at night. In fact it is often possible to see them at night while driving, their eyes reflected in the car's headlights. Just like cats, possums, owls and other larger creatures that hunt at night, a mirror-like structure in the back of eye reflects light back to its source and helps the eye function more efficiently at night.

*Wolf spiders are unusual in carrying their minute young with them on their backs, even as they hunt.*

# Wolf Spiders

*A most distinctive characteristic of wolf spiders is their nimble, fleet-footed style of hunting; by day they hide in burrows.*

The wolf spiders have a roving, nocturnal lifestyle that generally resembles that of some of the ancient spiders. Many even build silk-lined burrows with a lid, or else a 'collar' or levee of plant debris surrounding the entrance, returning to it at dawn and hiding in it through the day. Unlike the sluggish ancient spiders, however, they are extraordinarily swift and agile. They feed mainly on crawling insects, relying on speed, size and strength to run them down. They bite freely if provoked and some of the larger species may be dangerous to humans: indeed one close relative in Europe is lethal.

## Distribution and Features

Wolf spiders are virtually worldwide in distribution and there are at least 130 species in Australia. Some of the largest are nearly 3.5 cm in body length but most are medium sized, often brown or brownish in colour, with long agile legs and trim but rounded bodies. Many have striking patterns in muted tones of fawn, ochre, slate grey, brown and black on the carapace and abdomen. They have eight eyes, arranged in three rows: four in the topmost row and two each thereafter. The two eyes in the central row are very much bigger than the others.

# Huntsman Spiders

While often wrongly called tarantulas, huntsman spiders are those large, flat, rather flabby-looking spiders that frequently appear on the walls or ceilings of our houses at night. They are also common on the trunks of trees in forests and woodlands of all kinds. They tend to spend long periods of time motionless, then sidle sideways in exactly the sort of motion most calculated to upset an arachnophobe (a person with an extreme irrational fear of spiders). However, they are slow-moving, timid, extremely difficult to provoke and, so far as is known, they are harmless to humans. They are, on the other hand, deadly to flies, cockroaches and other unwanted insect visitors about the home.

*There are many different kinds of huntsman spiders but all of them have flattened bodies and long sprawling legs.*

## Form, Function and Harmony between the Sexes

The legs of huntsmen spiders sprawl oddly sideways, an arrangement that, together with their flattened bodies and crab-like gait, enables them to hide and move freely in extremely confined spaces, such as behind wall-boards or slabs of bark on trees. Such hidden spaces are their preferred habitat.

Males are only a little smaller than females and they usually differ little in appearance. Female huntsmen are unusual among spiders in that they are not aggressive to males and mated pairs remain together for some time, caressing and stroking each other. Huntsmen are also unusual in the length of their courtship ritual: mating may last for 7 hours or more.

**MATERNAL INSTINCTS**
A female huntsman spider wraps her greenish eggs in an egg-sac and then either remains with them or carries them around. When they hatch, the spiderlings remain with their mother for a time and share her prey.

# How do Spiders Use Silk?

*Spiders use silk for many purposes, notably as safety-lines, as snares to trap prey and to wrap their eggs in a protective cocoon, as here.*

Spiders are, above all, silk weavers. While some insects and certain other groups also weave with silk, the spider has evolved by far the most sophisticated apparatus for spinning silk and it is used in almost everything the spider does. All spiders use it at least to wrap their eggs and even wandering hunters that do not build webs meticulously lay down a safety-line of silk everywhere they go. Silk is also used to line burrows, to form retreats and snares, meshes for bundling up prey and packaging for sperm.

# How Strong and Flexible is Spiders' Silk?

*Extremely elastic and strong, spider silk has up to five times the tensile strength of steel.*

Spider silk is one of the most extraordinary substances in the animal kingdom. Some kinds are as much as five times stronger than a steel cable of the same diameter. Other kinds are among the most elastic substances known, easily coping with being stretched to nearly double their original length before breaking. The thickness of a silken thread varies according to type but it seldom exceeds three one hundred thousandths of a millimetre.

---

**AN INDIAN MYTH**

The Navajo people of North America are famous for their finely woven, brightly coloured blankets. Their folklore has it that the skill of weaving was taught to them in ancient times by the mythical Spider Woman. She stipulated that all blankets must contain a single small hole, a practice followed to this day.

# What is Spiders' Silk?

*E*'ssentially a complex protein, silk produced by spiders is a rapid-hardening fluid that is squirted under extraordinarily delicate control from a cluster of organs called spinnerets. Spinnerets are situated towards the end of the lower abdomen. There are at least six distinct types of silk and most spiders produce a combination of several — although, so far as is known, never all six. The various types are extruded for different purposes: building webs, shrouding prey, bundling eggs and so on.

## Silk Production

Spinnerets are highly mobile, and perhaps the easiest way of visualising what happens when a spider spins silk is to imagine that your fingertips have openings that can extrude silk like squeezing toothpaste from a tube, and that they can weave the strands together in various complicated ways by delicate manipulation as the silk emerges.

*The net-casting spider is so-called from the ingenious net it weaves of silk to throw over its victims.*

## Special Spinning Structures

Two distinctive anatomical structures, unique to modern spiders, aid in the production of silk: the cribellum and the calamistrum. The cribellum is a small disk connected to specialised silk glands and equipped with minute holes. Working rather on the general principle of a minute shower sprinkler, the cribellum is involved in the production of especially fine silk. Usually web-weaving spiders have a cribellum and roving hunters do not but there are some exceptions to this rule.

The calamistrum consists essentially of a row of minute hooks at the tips of the spider's hind pair of feet. These are used to comb, braid or fluff out the silk as it emerges from the spinnerets and before it hardens on contact with air.

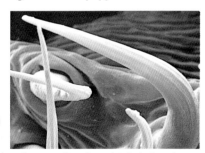

*Silk emerges from the spider's body through elaborate nozzles, called spinnerets, which are located at the tip of its abdomen.*

# Do Spiders have Enemies?

*Severe mite infestations may starve a spider. The sheer weight of numbers interfere with its ability to hunt.*

*T*he spider's silken orb-web is one of the most sophisticated and efficient prey-catching devices to be found in nature. Watching a spider patiently lying in wait at its centre, it is easy to form an impression of spiders as ultimate predators, masters of their world that need fear nothing. In fact, like other small animals, they are surrounded by enemies. Large spiders prey on smaller spiders as readily as on insects. There are also 'pirate' spiders that rob other spiders of their prey and 'assassin' spiders that specialise in hunting even larger species than themselves.

**PARASITES AND DISEASE**

Spiders are also prone to attack from a variety of different parasites, such as infestations of minute nematode worms and a host of bacterial and fungal diseases.

## Besieged by the Hordes

*S*piders are preyed upon by many mammals and birds, and ground-dwelling forms frequently fall victim to scorpions. Trapdoor spiders in their burrows are preyed upon by giant centipedes that have no hesitation in barging straight into the burrow and tackling its occupant head on. There are even huge, carnivorous, tunnelling crickets that simply crash straight through the burrow walls to snatch their spider.

Still more enemies are to be found among the insects that spiders mostly prey upon. Large robber flies may attack spiders in their webs, assassin bugs and praying mantids are serious threats to roving spiders, ants rob them of their eggs and tachinid flies and others lay their eggs on the bodies of living spiders — on hatching, their grubs burrow beneath the spider's skin and grow in its flesh.

*Insects sometimes turn the tables on spiders as shown by this bull-ant carrying a small spider back to its nest.*

# Why do Spiders Fear Wasps?

*P*erhaps the most relentless and persistent enemies of spiders are several groups of wasps, notably the sand wasps, ichneumon wasps and potter wasps. These wasps hunt spiders as food for their young. Typically, the wasp anaesthetises its victim by stinging it with its long ovipositor then drags its limp carcass back to its burrow where it lays an egg upon its inert body and seals it in. Paralysed, but still alive, the helpless spider is eaten by the wasp grub when it hatches.

## Horrible Ways to Die

There are many variations on this theme in Australia. Some wasps, for example, first excavate the nursery then seek a spider, while others first catch the spider then construct a burrow. In many species the female wasp habitually attacks spiders many times her size and will unhesitatingly enter the burrows of the largest trapdoor spiders. Often the spider seems aware of the threat and, making no attempt to fight back, cowers helplessly in its burrow or, if encountered on the surface, rushes about in apparent panic.

## Zombie Spiders

Some wasp species neither paralyse their victim nor drag it away. Instead they simply stun it, lay an egg on its body — taking care to place it where it cannot be dislodged — and leave. The spider recovers, the egg hatches and the grub proceeds to eat the spider alive. There are even tiny wasps that lay their eggs in spider's eggs, the spider's embryo providing food for the minute wasp grub as it grows.

*An unusual documentation of a wasp hunting, killing and finally burying its spider victim.*

# Sac Spiders

*Some sac spiders are quite large, with a body length of 3 cm or more.*

*T*he sac spiders are a group of spiders that look very much like wolf spiders and they behave in much the same way. Perhaps the best way of distinguishing these two groups of roving hunters is by the arrangement of their eyes: while sac spiders have eight small eyes arranged in two rows of four, the wolf spiders have two large eyes above a horizontal row of four.

Like wolf spiders, many sac spiders are of substantial size; some up to 3 cm in length. Also like wolf spiders, most sac spiders stalk their prey, then run it down and overwhelm it with a sudden dash. The claws of sac spiders are equipped with minute hair tufts that enables them to run nimbly over smooth vertical surfaces.

## A Large Group of Aggressive Spiders

The sac spiders are a very varied group with a worldwide distribution. Australia has nearly 400 species belonging to three families. Most are grey or brown in colour, although one introduced species common in houses is pale buff. Most hunt in the open and are active mainly at night. Rather than constructing permanent shelters, sac spiders build temporary retreats or 'sacs'. The sacs are hidden wherever the spider happens to be at dawn.

Many species are aggressive and have large jaws. Less timid than many spiders, some can easily be provoked into delivering a painful bite. Their large jaws can inject a substantial quantity of venom, which often results in local tissue damage and an ulcerous sore that may be slow to heal. Although the bite of some species may cause temporary illness, the venom is not known to be life-threatening to humans.

# White-tailed Spider

*The White-tailed Spider is easily identified by the pale tip to its abdomen.*

The colour of the White-tailed Spider varies from deep purple-brown to black, depending on age or the time since the last moult, but it can usually be readily identified by a distinctive white tip to the abdomen. The female is about 2 cm long, while the much smaller male is about 12 mm long.

This species inhabits woodlands of various kinds and usually shelters under the flaking bark of eucalypts, although it sometimes enters houses, especially in late summer. It hunts mainly at night and shelters by day in a tubular retreat of silk. It preys on insects and other spiders and especially targets spiders that build snares or low webs. It sits at the margins of such webs and tugs at the silk in imitation of the struggles of a captured insect, then seizes the spider when it comes to investigate.

## Widespread and Toxic

The White-tailed Spider occurs almost throughout Australia, including Tasmania, but is more common in the temperate zone than in the tropics. It also occurs in New Zealand.

Its venom is highly toxic to humans but its bite is probably not lethal; nevertheless, it carries a bacterium that causes severe ulcerous or necrotic sores around the site of the bite and these are extremely slow to heal.

> **TOO SMALL TO SEE**
> One of the commonest spiders in human habitation is so minute that it is seldom noticed and does not even have an ordinary English name. Barely 2 mm long, *Oecobius annulipes* is active at night. With careful searching it can sometimes be found, often motionless under a tiny flat web tucked into a window corner.

# Are Spiders Sociable?

Most spiders are solitary hunters but there are exceptions. Members of one entire almost worldwide family, the social spiders, live in communities and contribute their labour to a large communal web.

Other kinds of association between individuals are not unknown. There are some small orb-weavers, for example, in which both male and female live together in the same web, behaving almost as a mated pair. Also the webs of many large web-weavers are inhabited by numbers of very much smaller scavenging spiders that exist on whatever scraps the owner might leave behind after feeding.

# Are Spiders Warm-blooded?

Spiders are not warm-blooded. Like all other animals, except mammals and birds, their internal temperature normally follows that of the space around them. However, they can exert some influence on it. Some spiders exposed to strong sunlight, for example, may point the tip of their abdomen towards the sun, which reduces the total skin area exposed and so helps to prevent overheating.

*Some spiders cool down by holding their bodies end-on to the sun to minimise the surface area exposed.*

# How do 'Lungs' Dictate Lifestyle ?

*T*he spider's breathing apparatus has played a critical role in the evolution of spiders from ground burrowers to aerial web dwellers. Book-lungs are perfectly adequate for an animal spending most of its time in the high humidity of a burrow in the ground but they are inefficient in their use of water and web-weavers are often fully exposed to the drying influences of sun and wind.

At some point in their history, the modern spiders evolved an alternate breathing system whereby closable valves on the body wall led to a system of narrow passages that carried oxygen to all parts of the body. Modern spiders have retained one pair of the ancestral book-lungs but a crucial characteristic of them is that they also possess the newer, 'hi-tech' tracheal breathing system.

*High in her web, a garden spider is fully exposed to the drying effects of sun and wind.*

# Is Spider Silk Used for Anything?

*I*t has been calculated that when a spider's orb-web absorbs the impact of a fast-flying insect, it converts a momentum that would stop a jet aircraft if scaled up to comparable units of weight and speed. Human industry has thousands of uses for such a remarkable material but problems of mass production and collection have to date thwarted efforts to exploit it, except for small-scale use as crosshairs in telescopic gun-sights and similar instruments.

A promising recent development is the creation of a synthetic version of the spider's silk-producing gene. This gene can be inserted into the DNA of bacteria to produce 'biosilk' in the form of granules. In principle, this material can be dissolved and spun into fibres by the same means now used to produce rayon, nylon and other synthetic fibres.

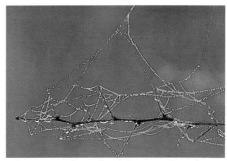

*The properties of strength and elasticity make spider's silk potentially useful to people.*

# Lattice-web Spiders

*Lattice-web spiders are best identified by their distinctive webs.*

Spiders of this group lack distinctive features of shape, colour or pattern. Most are dull greyish brown in colour and some resemble wolf spiders in general appearance except that their eight eyes are arranged in two rows of four and they have longer spinnerets.

Their webs, however, have a characteristic structure. Although basically a horizontal, finely woven sheet web, pinned to its support by a maze of vertical threads, the web as a whole is three-dimensional rather than the flat, two-dimensional structure most orb-weavers build.

Lattice-webs also differ in being built mainly of dry silk rather than sticky silk. They rely more on prey becoming disoriented and entangled than stuck fast, which means that the spider needs to react quickly in its attack. Such webs are especially effective at catching crawling or hopping insects.

## Webs Indoors and Out

Some lattice-web builders are very small but their sheet-like webs in the grass are often obvious on golf courses and similar places very early in the morning when they are made more visible in the dew.

Apart from the various native lattice-web spiders, there is one species that is an abundant foreigner, accidentally brought from Europe by humans and now virtually worldwide in distribution. Confusingly called the House Spider, it is not related to the Black House-spider (see page 67) but is similarly large, black and hairy. Common in houses, it builds big messy webs in secluded corners, often obvious by their 'dusty' appearance.

# Crinoline Spider

The Crinoline Spider is a light yellowish brown colour overall but intricate flecks and patterns on its body and legs break up its outline and make it hard to see against the rock faces that are its favourite habitat. The cephalothorax and abdomen are both rather round and flat and the spider is about 1 cm in total body length. The sexes are approximately equal in size but the male is noticeably slimmer and has longer legs. This species is widespread in eastern Australia, mainly east of the Great Dividing Range.

*The Crinoline Spider is one of the most common of the lattice-web spiders.*

## A Crafty Snare

The lattice web of the Crinoline Spider is often built on the roof of a shallow cave or under the overhang of a large boulder. It takes the form of a roughly circular sheet pinned at the edges so that, like a hammock, it bellies downward at the centre. The hub is pulled up and pinned to the support overhead in such a way that it forms an inverted funnel that narrows to a tube leading to a silk-lined retreat in which the spider spends most of its time. The web is closely woven and, depending on the species, rather resembles a hammock or even a hooped petticoat.

When an insect blunders into the net, the spider dashes from its retreat and out onto the underside of the web. It bites it through the net, hauls the victim through, bundles it in silk and either eats it on the spot or dangles it from a thread to be eaten later. It repairs the torn hole in the net and retires to its lair to await the next victim.

> **MULTIPURPOSE WEBS**
> Lattice-webs are not only extremely efficient prey-catching devices; they also help to protect the spiders from predators.

# Who are the Spiders' Relatives?

Spiders belong to a vast assemblage of animals known as arthropods, a group set apart from all other animals by two key features: they have many pairs of jointed legs (never less than three) and their bodies are contained in a mostly rigid external skin — in a sense these animals wear their skeletons on the outside. Apart from spiders, other arthropods include lobsters, crabs, insects, millipedes, centipedes, scorpions and an array of lesser known creatures. Their eight legs and their use of silk set spiders well apart from this assembly but their closest relatives include the scorpions, millipedes and centipedes.

*Scorpions are close relatives of spiders but differ most obviously in their long flexible tails.*

# A Tale of Two Tails

*Two-tailed spiders are very common but difficult to find.*

Although they are quite small and heavily camouflaged, with a bit of patient searching two-tailed spiders are easily found on the rough bark of tree trunks almost anywhere in coastal Australia. They have flat bodies, heart-shaped abdomens and their six eyes are raised up on turrets. Immediately identifiable by the extreme length of two of their spinnerets, these are about as long as the abdomen and extend rearward like a tail. These spinnerets are lined with silk spigots all along their inside edges and they are used to capture prey in a most unusual way.

When it locates an insect crawling on the bark, the two-tailed spider dashes up to it and turns its back so that the long, outspread spinnerets almost encircle it. The spider then drops two blobs of sticky silk on the bark and proceeds to scuttle crabwise around its victim at dizzying speed, ejecting swathes of silk as it goes, until the prey is completely entangled. The victim is dispatched and eaten on the spot, then the spider resumes its position to wait for another unwary victim.

# What is a Badge Spider?

*B*adge spiders are closely related to the huntsman spiders, which they resemble in general appearance except that their bodies are rounder and less flattened and their legs are less inclined to sprawl. The body length of a typical badge spider is about 2.5 cm. There are 25 or so species in Australia and they are very widespread. Although they live in holes in the ground, they clamber freely about on tree trunks and among shrubbery and foliage.

Badge spiders are often brightly coloured, especially in tones of yellow and orange and their legs are characteristically banded and marked in various ways with white, black, yellow and red. Their name is derived from the bold patterns of black, white, yellow and dull red on the underside of their abdomens, the colours arranged on a shield-shaped field in such a way that the result rather resembles a school badge.

Unlike huntsman spiders, badge spiders are suspected of having a dangerous bite. Although little is known of their venom and its effects, and no fatalities have as yet apparently been reported, they should be treated warily.

*Badge spiders may resemble huntsman spiders but the 'badge' on the undersides is distinctive.*

# Jumping Spiders

*Among the best known of all spiders, jumping spiders come in a wide range of colours and shapes.*

Jumping spiders make up the largest family group of all spiders, with more than 4,000 known species worldwide. Common in almost every type of habitat, they are active hunters of prey on the ground, on the bark of trees and among foliage. They often enter houses, too, especially in the tropics. A few are medium in size but most are easily overlooked because of their small body size, typically around 4–5 mm long. Some species are brightly coloured but most are a nondescript grey or dull brown. Some have striking facial markings such as white or reddish 'goggles' around the eyes. Many bear tufts of hair on the front of their cephalothorax that form bushy 'eyebrows', 'moustaches' or similar facial adornments.

## Major Characteristics

The name 'jumping spider' is unusually apt as the ability to jump in these spiders is their most prominent characteristic. They usually capture their prey, which consists of a wide range of small insects, by means of a sudden prodigious leap.

Although jumping spiders have three rows of eyes arranged in a pattern of four, two and two, the middle pair are normally very much larger than the others. They are much more long-sighted than other spiders and have large 'aware' eyes that tend to goggle engagingly at you as their owner peers from behind a lamp or some other small item of furniture. Even people who are afraid of spiders often feel considerably less intimidated by jumping spiders than by others.

**EYEBALLING SPIDERS**
If you examine a jumping spider with a magnifying glass, it is quite likely to peer right back at you.

# Fiddle-back Spiders

*Fiddle-back spiders get their name from a fancied resemblance in body shape to a violin or fiddle.*

*T*he fiddle-back or violin spiders get their name from the fact that, viewed from above, the shape and markings of their bodies bear some resemblance to a fiddle. There are about 20 species elsewhere in the world but none are native to Australia. However, the group is of some importance because two species have been accidentally introduced into Australia. They are often common in homes and gardens, especially in eastern and southern Australia, and they should be regarded as dangerous.

## Habits, Appearance and Toxicity

Like wolf spiders, fiddle-back spiders are roving hunters that do not weave snares or permanent lairs and they prey mainly on crawling insects. In their original home of Europe and North America some species are called recluse spiders, an apt summation of their habits.

Fiddle-back spiders somewhat resemble wolf spiders in appearance as well as habits but they have six eyes arranged in three groups of two; these curve around the forward slope of the head. The body is flattened, light fawn in colour and about 7–8 mm in length. The legs are long and slender, and clad in minute short hairs.

Fiddle-back spiders are usually shy and non-aggressive and their fangs are too small to inflict a serious bite on an adult human. Nonetheless, even small quantities of venom may result in illness and cause severe tissue damage in the vicinity of the bite. Bites may result in skin ulcers, several centimetres across, that are difficult to treat and sometimes take months to heal. Fatalities occasionally occur overseas, although none appear, so far, to have been reported in Australia.

# When is a Spider an Ant?

*Spiders of several groups have evolved an uncanny resemblance to ants as a device to conceal their identity from their favourite prey.*

When it's in disguise, of course. Ants are abundant insects in almost every Australian habitat and two distinct groups of spiders have converged on a diet in which ants feature almost exclusively. These spiders have evolved a variety of remarkable devices to exploit their prey and most of these involve disguising themselves to better penetrate ant colonies and move unhindered within them.

## Masters of Disguise

One small group of these ant specialists are members of the sac spider family. The others are derived from jumping spiders. Both have achieved a remarkable similarity in body shape to that of the ants on which they prey. There is a pinched-in section midway along their cephalothorax, which presents the illusion of the ant's three body sections rather than the spider's two. Since spiders have no antennae but ants do and they have eight legs not six, these spiders put their extra pair of legs to use by waving them about constantly in front of them, just as ants do with their antennae. These legs, disguised as antennae, even mimic the colour and pattern of ants' antennae.

The ant-mimicking spiders enjoy a double dividend from their disguise because many ants are unpalatable to birds and are usually avoided by other predators, too. So the spider benefits not only by easy access to its prey but it also 'borrows' the ant's immunity from attack by predators.

### CAN SPIDERS FLY?

Spiders lack wings but some jumping spiders, especially one called the flying spider, have a movable 'flap' on each side of the abdomen. What they are used for remains uncertain: maybe they enable the spider to jump farther in a manner similar to that used by gliding possums or they may play a role in courtship.

# How is Camouflage Different from Mimicry?

Camouflage is very common among animals, following the general principle that of the three basic strategies for dealing with a predator — fight, run or hide — the last takes much less energy. From a predator's perspective, too, stalking prey is much easier if it blends in well with its background. Camouflage that relies on blending with the background is referred to as 'crypsis' and may involve either colour or shape or both. The bird-dung spiders, for example, are both shaped and coloured to closely resemble a bird dropping.

*This bark spider relies heavily on its colouring and patterning to blend in with its background.*

## A Confusing Disguise

Mimicry, on the other hand, arises when a harmless animal evolves a resemblance to a dangerous one or when a dangerous animal looks like a harmless one. In the first case, a predator may hesitate before attacking until certain of the animal's identity. Hesitation may foil the attack, so the mimic profits from the deception. In the second case, a predator evolves a resemblance to its prey so that it can get closer to it before launching an attack. Ant-mimicking spiders, for example, have evolved a successful deception because they are accepted by their sociable prey, ants, as 'just another face in the crowd'.

*Some spiders take camouflage by concealment to an extreme having evolved elaborate and often bizarre body structures, like this twig spider, which fools predators by its striking resemblance to a twig.*

# SIT-AND-WAIT SPIDERS

# How do Spiders Care for their Young?

*A mother huntsman spider guards her eggs as they hatch.*

*A*s in other animal groups, it varies. Parental care begins even before the eggs hatch and most spiders take a great deal of trouble securing safety and appropriate conditions for their eggs. These are almost invariably wrapped in a cocoon of silk, which is often elaborate: bird-dung spiders, for example, seal them in hardened capsules. Some spiders stand guard on their egg-sacs until they hatch and some roving species carry them with them wherever they go.

Parental care after hatching is a little less common but some trapdoor spiders share their mother's burrow for some time after hatching and wolf spiders can often be found wandering over the ground with their broods of spiderlings clinging to their backs. Some species, such as the Crinoline Spider, feed their young mouth to mouth and in some spider species the young eventually cannibalise their mother.

# Are Spiders Scented?

*I*n the case of two unrelated groups of spiders, the answer is most definitely yes but not in order to attract one another. Both the bird-dung spiders and the bolas spiders commonly use a highly unusual trick to lure their prey within range.

Female moths release potent chemicals called pheromones; these can attract male moths from a considerable distance. In this particular mating game the spiders intervene by manufacturing and releasing identical pheromones so that male moths in pursuit of a scent trail instead of finding a mate at journey's end may meet a gruesome consummation of another sort in the jaws of the spider.

*Bird-dung spiders are able to mimic the sexual perfumes their victims rely on to find each other.*

## SUBTLE CONCOCTIONS
Some spiders even use different pheromones to lure different moths, according to season, and one species goes even further, releasing specific pheromones to lure moths of the appropriate size to suit its particular growth stage.

# Do Spiders Spit?

*A* worldwide family of about 200 species of spiders are unique in that its members catch their prey by squirting a sticky fluid at it. The fluid is not silk and does not emerge from the spinnerets; instead, it originates in glands associated with the venom glands. Propelled from orifices in the fangs with a rapid side-to-side vibration, the sticky fluid is ejected in two zigzag streams over the victim, pinning it to the ground. Once immobilised, the prey is bitten with the fangs in the usual spider fashion.

There are several native spitting spiders in Australia but they are all rare and little known. The only common species is a household creature that has been accidentally introduced by humans to almost everywhere from its original home in Europe.

Although common, these spiders hunt mainly at night and hide during the day. About 6 mm in total body length, they have plump, rounded abdomens and the carapace is distinctively domed. Their chief prey consists of cockroaches, silverfish and other crawling insects but they sometimes also catch moths and similar night-flying insects. Spitting spiders have spinnerets but they use silk only for bundling up their eggs, which they carry around clasped between their palps and chelicerae until they hatch.

*Spitting spiders can often be identified by an extremely domed carapace, bulging from the size of the 'spit' glands underneath.*

# Crab Spiders

*Crab-like in gait and outline, crab spiders wait patiently for their victims to come to them.*

Like jumping spiders, crab spiders are hunters but most do not stalk their prey, instead preferring to wait in ambush for it. They build no webs and use silk only for safety-lines and for wrapping their eggs. There are nearly 150 known species of crab spiders in Australia and they are very common and widespread.

## Description and Eyesight

Crab spiders vary in size but few have bodies longer than about 1.5 cm. Their skin may be lumpy or spiny but seldom hairy. They are crab-like in shape and they also tend to scuttle sideways as crabs do. Their two front pairs of legs, which are used for clasping prey, are usually very much longer than their hind pairs, which are used mainly for clinging to the perch. In most species, camouflage is well developed. Species living on the trunks of trees often look very like a scrap of bark, while ground-dwellers may closely mimic fungi or fallen leaves in colour and pattern.

Like jumping spiders, crab spiders rely heavily on vision for detecting their prey: their eight eyes, arranged in two rows of four, are very prominent. Crab spiders have the unusual ability among spiders to rotate their eyes independently of each other.

> **A FLAKY DISGUISE**
>
> A group of small crab spiders, called *Stephanopis*, have rough, spiny skins that are coloured so as to make them almost impossible to find on the bark of trees on which they live. To enhance this disguise, they fasten onto their bodies flakes of bark or, where trunks have been blackened by fire, minute scraps of charcoal.

# Flower Spiders

*Flower spiders are a group of crab spiders characterised by their habit of waiting in ambush among flower petals.*

*F*lower spiders are members of the crab spider family but, unlike other crab spiders, their favourite hunting habitat is flowers. Here these spiders lie in wait for their prey, the colouration of their bodies extraordinarily closely matched with that of the petals on which they sit. The camouflage is so good that they rely on it entirely, waiting fully exposed on the petal and making no other attempt to hide. Because of this strong resemblance to flower petals, some of these spiders are vividly coloured. The most common colours are shades of green, white and yellow.

## Looking for a Flower Spider

Very common and widespread, flower spiders are not at all hard to find with a little patience but it calls for minute, thorough, petal-by-petal examination. One trick that sometimes works to is to pay particular attention to any small insect perched on a flower that seems unnaturally still — it may be that it is being sucked dry by a flower spider. Sometimes, a telltale pile of insect remains on the ground below a flower give away the presence of a flower spider.

# What do Spiders Eat?

*Like this jumping spider subduing an ant, insects make by far the most important prey of almost all spiders.*

*A*ll spiders are predators and most will eat almost anything they can kill. The vast majority prey on insects but quite a number prey on other spiders, too, and many will feed on scorpions, millipedes and a host of similar small animals. A few spiders are scavengers that loiter like jackals in the outer margins of other spiders' webs, waiting for a chance at the leftovers.

Although there are some spiders that are large enough to overpower very small mammals or reptiles and some occasionally catch and eat small birds trapped in their webs, warm-blooded animals are not a regular diet item for spiders.

# How Many Kinds of Spiders are There?

*S*piders constitute one of the most abundant and successful of all animal groups. They occur in virtually all terrestrial environments in all regions except the polar ice-caps. The current total is around about 35,000 species — and we are still counting. There are many parts of the world, especially tropical rainforests,

*Many spiders are sober-hued, but a few, like this jewel spider, rival birds and butterflies in their brilliant colours and bold patterns.*

where the spider fauna is virtually unknown and probably many thousands of species still await discovery. Australia has about 2,000 known species.

# How Old are the Oldest Spiders?

Spiders do not fossilise well and the early fossil record is very difficult to interpret. However, it seems clear that the basic spider body plan was laid down some 350 million years ago when scorpions first appear in the fossil record but the earliest fossil that is unarguably a spider is from deposits about 300 million years old. Many of the ancient spiders can be traced back some 250 million years but it seems probable that the modern spider's web-making skills did not arise until about 150 million years ago when the first flies evolved to blunder into the first spider webs.

# Do Spiders Really Eat Birds?

Occasionally they do. Certainly one or two species from South America, Australia and elsewhere are known to prey on birds, among other small animals but birds are not a common food item for spiders. Nevertheless, some Australian spiders are large enough to capture small sleeping birds and the large webs of several Australian species of golden orb-weavers are strong enough to occasionally capture small flying birds, such as sunbirds and silvereyes, and these are sometimes attacked and eaten.

*Australian bird-eating spiders are misleadingly named, and seldom include birds in their diet — but there are other spiders that some-times do.*

> **MONSTER SPIDERS**
> The world's biggest spider is a bird-eating spider from South America with a body length of 9 cm and legs spanning 28 cm. Several other spiders are large enough to catch and eat small birds, including several Australian species, but many more are of moderate size and thousands of species are minute — barely a millimetre or two in total length.

# Bird-dung Spiders

*Confusingly, several unrelated species of spiders share a marked resemblance to a bird dropping.*

Some spiders of several groups are aptly named the bird-dung spiders because of their extraordinarily close resemblance, in colour, size and shape, to an ordinary bird dropping. They huddle motionless on their perch with their legs tucked in tightly to their lumpy bodies and cling stubbornly to the deception even when gently poked or prodded. The various species differ in size but most are about 8 mm long.

Bird-dung spiders are ambush hunters but some species hunt by day, waiting patiently for some unwary fly or similar insect to come within range. They then make a lightning-fast leap, seizing their prey by clasping it in their spiny front limbs. Others are active at night and one group uses pheromones (see page 52) to lure its prey, its diet apparently consisting of nothing more than one particular group of moths.

## A Fastidious Egg-sac Maker

Female bird-dung spiders expend an unusual amount of time and trouble on their egg-sacs. The details vary among species but in one group the female lays several hundred eggs on a silken sheet, then bundles them up in large quantities of fluffy silk. When suitably padded, she ties the bundle up into a ball with a different type of silk. Finally, she coats the ball with a special body fluid that weathers to a hard, brownish, waterproof shell, and dangles the whole thing by a thread among foliage. The ball may be bigger than the spider that made it and over several weeks she manufactures up to ten or more other egg-sacs just like the first.

# Triangular Spiders

*Triangular spiders are easily told by their colourful, triangle-shaped bodies.*

The triangular spiders are a good example of a simple name saying all that's necessary: their abdomens are indeed obviously and almost uniquely triangular. They are also glossy, almost completely hairless, brightly coloured, usually red or orange, and often patterned with bold white or yellow spots or similar patterns. There are about six species in Australia, all less than 10 mm in body length.

The limbs of triangular spiders are unusual in structure: the two hind pairs are short for firm anchorage on their perch and the spiny front two pairs are longer and held arched out and forward: looking almost like a scorpion's nippers, these are for seizing prey. Although you would need a magnifying glass to see them clearly, the configuration of their small dark eyes is also unusual, with two eyes close together in the centre of the carapace and one pair well off on each outer margin.

## Habitat and Prey Capture

Triangular spiders are common and widespread, especially in eucalypt forests and woodlands. In lifestyle they resemble crab spiders and flower spiders, hanging about in plain view on leaves, blades of grass, bracken fronds, flowers and similar places, often within a metre or two from the ground. They wait patiently for unwary insects to come within range and pounce on their prey like a cat on a mouse. Also like crab and flower spiders, they are completely harmless to humans.

### ABANDONING THE WEB

Although triangular spiders are closely related to web-weaving spiders, they have abandoned their web-weaving lifestyle for a life of hijacking and now use silk only for safety-lines and for wrapping their eggs.

# Net-casting Spiders

*The net-casting spiders are often called ogre-faced spiders because of their extraordinary alien faces.*

Often also known as ogre-faced spiders, net-casting spiders are generally rather large, with unusually slender bodies and very long, stick-like legs. Their movements are generally deliberate and they are easily recognised by their enormous central pair of eyes, very much bigger than the three pairs of conventional spider's eyes on either side. This arrangement of eyes give the spider, seen head-on, a rather owl-like look or, more fancifully perhaps, an ogre, hence its alternative name.

## A Curious Hunting Strategy

Most net-casting spiders are greyish or dull brown in colour, often mottled or marbled in various ways but seldom with any patches of bright colour. Active only at night, they do not build permanent webs. Instead, they build small webs of cribellate silk on a framework that they hold by the tips of their first two pairs of legs.

Their capture technique is astonishing. Hanging head-downwards, the spider waits immobile for an insect to crawl below. At the appropriate moment, it lunges down and spreads its legs wide to stretch the net; it then dumps the whole lot onto its unfortunate victim, pinning it to the ground. The spider rapidly bundles it up in silk to immobilise it, bites it to death and eats it.

# Bolas Spiders

*I*t takes real patience to find a bolas spider, although they are very common across much of eastern Australia, even in towns and cities. During the day they hide in the foliage of trees within a few metres of the ground. Depending on the species, females are only around 10–14 mm in total length but the minute males are only roughly a tenth of this size.

Bolas spiders have few obvious identifying characteristics but most species have comparatively large, spherical abdomens; many are whitish or at least pale and some have brightly coloured abdomens. Sometimes their relatively enormous spindle-shaped egg-sacs, which are many times bigger than the parent spider, are more obvious than the spider itself.

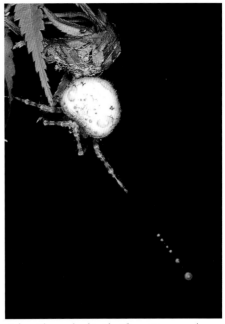

*Bolas spiders are hard to identify on appearance alone, but all doubts disappear on watching their astonishing capture technique.*

## Prey Capture Lasso-style

Bolas spiders hunt at night. Like the bird-dung spiders, they use pheromones (see p. 52) to lure their prey within range but their remarkable capture technique is unique. The spider dangles from a horizontal silken cable and lowers a single thread of very elastic silk, about 5 cm in length, towards the ground. The thread is beaded with sticky droplets along its length with an extra large gobbet at its end.

When a moth approaches within range, the spider whirls its thread like a cowboy twirling a lasso, lets it fly and ensnares its victim on the sticky thread. It then 'plays' its catch like a fly-fisherman playing a trout, reeling the line in and paying it out, until the moth can only dangle, helpless with exhaustion, to be hauled up and eaten.

### HARD OR STICKY SILKS

One significant distinction between types of silk is that between cribellate and viscid silk. Cribellate silk hardens dry on contact with air and is believed to be the most ancient form. Viscid silk, on the other hand, remains sticky indefinitely, even after exposure to air, and is thought to be one of the spiders' more recent 'inventions'.

# SNARE MAKERS

# Do Spiders Migrate?

*Australian wolf spiders are known to migrate: the 'how' is known but so far the 'when' 'where' and 'why' remain mysterious.*

Some do, although perhaps not quite in the sense ordinarily understood. In parts of Australia, adult wolf spiders travel by ballooning, using the same device used by many baby spiders to disperse. Under appropriate climatic conditions, they climb to a suitably high point and begin paying out a line of gossamer silk until it is long enough to be caught by the breeze. Then, kite-like, they are carried off. However, almost nothing is known of the circumstances, function or destination of such movements.

Wolf spiders certainly have at least part of the equipment needed to migrate. They habitually cover a great deal of ground on their nightly high-speed hunting forays, yet at dawn they find their way back to their own burrows. Their eyes are sensitive to polarised light, which forms patterns in the night sky that can be used to navigate. Polarised light is invisible to human eyes but it is known that homing pigeons use this same sensitivity as part of their arsenal of sensory equipment in finding their way back to their lofts.

*A Marine Spider's silk-lined hole is designed to trap air for the spider to breathe once the tide rises.*

---

### SUBMARINE BUBBLE

The Marine Spider, a common species around the northern shores of Australia, lives among rocks or coral in the intertidal zone between high- and low-water marks. It forages among rock pools, driftwood and seaweed when the tide is low, then seals itself into a silk-lined hole full of trapped air to rest while the tide is high.

# Fishing with Spider Thread

One small group of spiders are web-weavers but they have reduced the web to a single strand of silk. They belong to the same family as the wheel-web spiders (see page 68) but they use a very different and more complicated way of capturing their prey.

Sticky and very elastic, the thread is anchored at one end to a twig or some similar support and pulled taught by the spider's forelegs, allowing the slack to dangle freely beneath its body. It then sits immobile until an insect perches on the thread; then it promptly lets go. Released from tension, the thread whips back and entangles its victim in sticky silk. It is then quickly reeled in and eaten.

Another small spider in the same group does the same thing a little differently: it first lays a strand between two fixed points, then bites the line in two, using its own body to bridge the gap. It then waits, holding the ends tight in outstretched front and back legs respectively. When an insect alights, it rapidly slackens and hauls in several times to send a standing wave down the line, which entangles the prey. It then reacts with astonishing nimbleness, running down the line, paying out more from its spinnerets behind it while rapidly gathering it in front, to reach its prey.

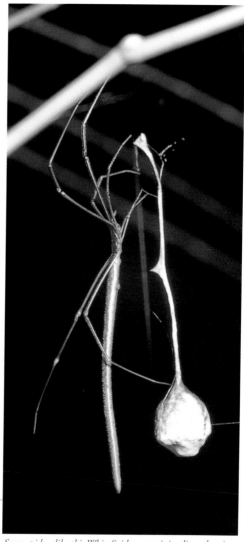

*Some spiders like this Whip Spider are minimalists when it comes to webs, using a single strand of silk with which to capture prey. This female has her egg-sac hanging alongside.*

# Lace-web Spiders

*Lace-web spiders build intricate webs that rely on entanglement rather than stickiness to capture their prey.*

*L*ace-web spiders have acquired their name from the fluffy, tangled, lace-like snares they build. These are often found in homes, usually tucked into some secluded corner such as a window ledge or behind furniture. There are 60 or more species of these spiders in Australia and they are common in almost all environments, especially in forests and woodlands. Most live on the ground or near it and the group includes some members that live in caves.

## Spider and Snare Description

Few lace-web spiders are more than about 1.5 cm in length and most are considerably smaller. The abdomen is oval-shaped and the cephalothorax high and domed, usually with a glossy carapace. Their eyes are arranged in two rows of four. A typical lace-web spider varies from greyish brown to black in colour, often with faint chevron-shaped markings on the abdomen and cephalothorax.

A lace-web spider's snare is roughly triangular, its threads radiating outward and crisscrossed with multiple zigzagging threads. Although the web contains sticky threads, insects captured in it are trapped more by their joints, spines and bristles becoming entangled in the multiple threads than by being held fast with 'glue'. The moment an insect's struggles vibrate the web, the spider dashes out to dispatch its victim.

# Black House-spider

The Black House spider is a species of lace-web spider that could very easily be mistaken for a Sydney Funnel-web, being big, black and more or less similar in shape. It also lives in a roughly purse-shape silken lair that approximately fits the description of a funnel-web's home. The resemblance is made even more striking by the fact that its bite can produce alarming symptoms in some humans, including severe pain, shock, muscle cramps, copious sweating and vomiting. However, these symptoms are usually temporarily severe rather than serious and the bite is not known to be lethal. It should nevertheless be regarded as moderately dangerous.

Despite the broad similarities to a funnel-web, it differs greatly in detail.

*One of the most common domestic spiders, the Black House-spider is not native to Australia.*

Most obviously it is substantially smaller: females are only about 1.8 cm long, males about half that size. Also, the chelicerae are proportionately much smaller.

## Habitat and Sedentary Behaviour

As its names suggest, the Black House-spider is common in houses and other buildings and a favoured site is the corner of a window or skylight. Here the lair is tucked into the corner and its snare radiates outwards. It is also common in gardens and parks, and sometimes occurs in bushland. The species is not native to Australia but was accidentally introduced by humans from its original home in Europe.

Unless forced to move for some reason, females live their entire lives in the same lair. Courtship is harmonious by comparison with many spiders and a successful male suitor may live with a female for some time in her web, mating frequently over several days.

67

# Wheel-web Spiders

*A typical wheel-web differs most obviously from other webs in being horizontal rather than vertical.*

Wheel-web spiders have a world-wide distribution. They are common in forests and woodlands of all kinds across Australia, although we have only about 13 known species. Inconspicuous in colour and pattern, most are very small and few exceed about 1 cm in body length. They earn their name from the shape of their distinctive, flimsy, wheel-like webs, normally built horizontally or slightly inclined in grass or shrubbery. Wheel-web spiders are unusual in several ways.

## Some Interesting Characteristics

To begin with, most are easily identified by the extraordinary length of their front legs; the other six are very much shorter. They usually hold these long legs straight out in front of them as they rest in their typical pose, immobile and hanging upside down at the hub and on the underside of their webs. They seldom leave their webs and seem unable to walk on a flat surface.

Alone among all spiders, wheel-web spiders lack poison glands. Although unusually meticulous in first wrapping their prey to subdue it, they kill captured insects by biting them and then inject digestive enzymes in the conventional spider fashion but they do not inject venom.

Wheel-web spiders have an intriguing anomaly in their web construction. Although their webs resemble those of orb-weavers — which might be considered a relatively modern feature — they are woven from cribellate silk, which is thought to be the most ancient form of silk, evolved by the earliest spiders millions of years before there were any flying insects for webs to catch.

# Daddy Long-legs

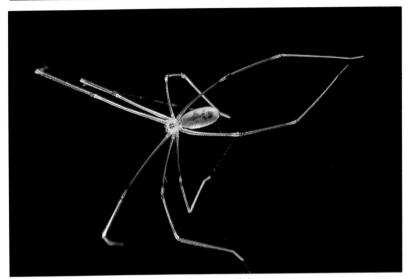

*The Daddy long-legs' most obvious identifying feature is spelled out in its name.*

Daddy long-legs are immediately obvious from their enormously long, spindly legs but, viewed under a magnifying glass, they are also distinctive in having eight pearly eyes arranged in two outer groups of three with a central group of two. These spiders often live in houses, where they build irregular webs so flimsy as to be overlooked, even though they are extremely common. Australia's most common species has a worldwide distribution, having been accidentally transported almost everywhere from its native home in Europe.

## Ingenious Predator Ploy

The spider rests all day head downwards in the centre of its web. When disturbed, it usually responds by setting up a rapid, vibratory, rotary motion in the web. The general effect is rather like bouncing up and down very rapidly on a trampoline while still holding onto it with hands and feet but the motion is circular as well. This performance is dizzying to watch; the spider becomes merely a blur of rapid motion in the centre of the web. It seems impossible that any enemy could move fast enough to catch it, which presumably is the whole idea.

### TOXIC BUT TINY

The daddy long-legs has fangs that are far too short to penetrate human skin and its venom glands are minute. It is a timid species that would much rather run than fight. All of these features are just as well because, drop for drop, a daddy long-legs' venom ranks among the most highly toxic of all spiders.

# Comb-footed Spiders

*Most comb-footed spiders are dark, mostly hairless and have plump, rounded abdomens.*

*T*he comb-footed spiders get their name from a series of spines on the hindlegs, which function as a sort of comb. They rake the silk out into wide swathes as it leaves the spinnerets and use it to wrap quickly around a victim to subdue its struggles.

The comb-footed spiders form a worldwide group represented in Australia by at least 90 species; members include the infamous Red-back Spider. All these spiders are mostly small or medium in size, seldom more than about 1.5 cm in length. They have globular abdomens and relatively small fangs. Their poison, however, is extremely virulent. Some species seem afraid of nothing and will unhesitatingly attack even very large, dangerous insects such as wasps, which much larger garden spiders hastily cut free of their webs when captured.

## Sticky Trap Webs

Comb-footed spiders are also called scaffold-web or tangle-web spiders after the distinctive structure of their webs. On casual examination these appear messy and haphazard but they are in fact carefully structured on an ingenious principle. The web is essentially an intricate piece of horizontal scaffolding or trellis suspended some centimetres above the ground. Numerous vertical threads are pinned to the ground and held taut by the scaffold above. These threads are strongly elastic and have beads of glue at the bottom. Any wandering insect below that brushes against a thread is held fast by the glue. The lower bond breaks and the recoil of the elastic thread flicks it into the air. Its struggles trigger neighbouring threads, which also snap and attach until the victim is hopelessly entangled. It is then hauled up and eaten.

# Red-back Spider

*A Red-back Spider is usually easily identified by its black, shiny, red-marked abdomen.*

Often regarded as the same species as the Kapito of New Zealand and the Black Widow of North America, the Red-back Spider is very common around human habitation throughout much of Australia. Favourite hiding places of this comb-footed spider include secluded window-sills, outdoor barbecues, letterboxes, outhouses and any place where litter or garden rubbish accumulates. Red-backs are easily identified by their shiny, pea-shaped, black or dark brown bodies, often with a bright red or orange patch on the top and bottom of the abdomen. Females are about 1.4 cm in body length; males are barely 3 mm.

## A Serious Bite

Several factors contribute to making the famous Red-back Spider less dangerous to humans than the notorious Sydney Funnel-web (see page 21) but it is safer to regard any bite from a red-back as a serious emergency. Professional medical help should be sought as quickly as possible. Modern antivenenes are very effective and, promptly administered, usually make recovery uneventful in a healthy adult, although complications may arise in the case of very young or very old victims. Hundreds of people are bitten every year in Australia but no fatalities have been reported in decades.

Although the red-back's venom is extraordinarily toxic, its fangs are small and the total quantity delivered in a bite may be very small. Also red-backs are usually timid and prefer to run and hide rather than stand and fight. Most bites occur when contact is entirely accidental, as when handling garden litter without the protection of gloves.

> **TOO SMALL TO COUNT**
> Only female Red-backs are dangerous: the males are minute and their fangs are unable to penetrate human skin.

# How do Spiders Court?

*A pair of orb-weaving spiders (the male is on the right) go through their intricate preparations for mating.*

*C*ourtship behaviour varies enormously among spiders. In some species, such as close relatives of the common house spider, the female is entirely submissive. Where the two sexes are almost of equal size a male may simply walk towards a female, tapping her web with his pedipalps as he goes. If receptive, she promptly huddles down with her legs folded and he drags her off to a suitable place for mating. Other female spiders are so enormous compared with their tiny spouses that they seem hardly aware that anything is going on during mating.

## Courting Danger

At the other extreme, many female garden spiders react savagely to courting males. These males need to be agile to avoid being killed and eaten. Only through sheer persistence do many of them succeed in mating; tirelessly they must dodge her charges until she finally submits. Another approach, adopted by many of the web-weavers, is for the male to initiate courtship by rhythmically plucking one of the 'spokes' of the female's web with his feet.

Still other males succeed by performing rituals. This is especially prevalent among jumping spiders. With intricate signalling movements of their outstretched pedipalps and their first pair of legs, they perform an extremely elaborate 'dance' that may go on for several hours before mating is attempted. Such displays may be reinforced by a spider's bright colours or bizarre tufts of hair.

Only a few spider species, such as some of the smaller orb-weavers, appear to form anything close to a pair bond.

**A HANDY DEVICE**

With certain aggressive female spiders, diversion tactics are a handy device. Before attempting to mate, males may catch an insect and gift-wrap it for presentation to the female. They then mate with her while she is absorbed in eating her meal.

# How do Spiders Mate?

*F*rom the male's perspective, spiders must mate with considerable caution. In many species, the female spider vastly outweighs her mate and she is very likely to eat him unless he takes elaborate precautions to prevent it. In other species, the male's lifespan is brief, extending little beyond the time needed to find a mate. There are even some spiders in which males undergo their first few moults in the egg even before hatching. They are thus well on their way to reaching sexual maturity before female eggs hatch a short time later.

> **SPIDER-STYLE LOVEMAKING**
> The duration of the mating act varies enormously among different groups of spiders. Among garden spiders it may take only a few seconds but some huntsmen take six hours or more.

## Pocket Sex

Male spiders lack anything resembling a penis; instead they use their palps to transfer their sperm to a receptive female. Among spiders generally, the male builds a small web and weaves a sort of apron over it. Ejecting his sperm onto this apron, he then siphons it up into a special pocket in each of his palps. He then goes in search of a female. During mating, he uses his palps to transfer his sperm directly into the female's reproductive organs.

*A golden orb-weaver pair mating; notice the enormous size difference between the sexes.*

# WEB-WEAVERS

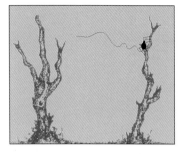

# What is an Orb-web?

*A*n artefact of the web-weavers, the orb-web is the name given to the most sophisticated snare built by spiders. The most consistent feature of a typical orb-web is a horizontal cable at the top linking two bushes or trees from which the rest of the structure is suspended. Most often, the spider establishes this foundation by taking up an appropriate position and paying out a length of light silk until it is caught by the breeze and carried across a gap to snag on some fixed point opposite, such as a branch or twig. This may need several attempts but sooner or later a line is established firmly enough to carry the spider's weight. The spider fixes it to its perch, then travels along the thread, spinning a second stronger cable as it goes.

## Establishing Framework

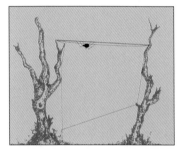

The next step is to spin a third thread across the gap, this one loose enough to sag considerably below the other two. The spider follows this thread until it reaches the centre point. There it fixes a new thread and uses it to drop directly downwards until it finds a suitable anchor point below. The structure is now a Y-shape suspended below a horizontal foundation cable: the central point of the Y establishes the hub of the web and the three 'arms' of the Y establish its first 'spokes'; more are then added until there may be anything from 20 to 60 spokes, depending on the species.

## Spinning the Scaffolding

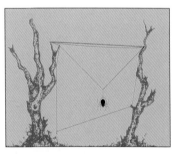

The third main stage of construction is to lay a continuous spiral of silk thread, working from near the centre outward to the edge of the web. This serves as a sort of

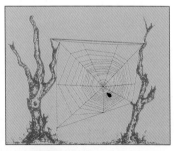

*Construction of an orb web: the spider lays the bridge line then reinforces it and builds the frame. A Y-shaped structure is anchored to the bottom, further spokes are added and the spiral web is completed.*

scaffolding for the final stage. Up to this point in construction the spider has used only dry 'construction-grade' silk. Some spiders eat the scaffolding spiral of their orb-web as they work; other spiders leave it standing.

## Laying the Trap

Finally the spider lays down the spiral of sticky, insect-catching silk, working from the outer margins inward. As each length of sticky thread is laid, and before pinning it to the spoke, the spider snaps it taut with a flick of her hindleg, causing the sticky coating to break up into minute globules along its length, like the beads on a necklace.

Most spiders finish up by making some adjustments to the hub. They then take up a position at the centre of the web or move to a hidden lair off to one side, depending on the species. All they must do then is to wait for the first flying insect to blunder into the net and become entangled.

# How do Spiders Avoid Web Entanglement?

*A* careless spider could indeed become entangled in its web every bit as thoroughly as its prey. That in fact it does not rests chiefly on three factors. Firstly, the spider always works on 'tiptoe', careful never to allow its body to touch the web. Secondly, its legs and feet are coated with a thin film of oil which does not adhere to the sticky silk. Thirdly, each foot carries a special hook at its tip: latched and twisted slightly, this hook tensions the thread and holds the spider securely.

*Like a miniature bicycle wheel, a typical orb-web is suspended vertically in bushes or trees.*

# Long-jawed Spiders

*The extended chelicerae of the long-jawed spiders are a good identifying feature. They are used in mating.*

*A*ptly named, the long-jawed spiders they are easily identified by their unusually long, forward-pointing chelicerae. Sometimes called the four-jawed spiders, their palps are extremely long, almost long enough to be mistaken for an extra pair of legs. Everything about these distinctive spiders is long and lean: the abdomen is exceptionally slender and the legs are extremely long and spindly. Size is variable in the group but one especially common and widespread species is about 1.2 cm in body length. Few species are brightly coloured; in most the abdomen is grey, brown or mahogany red.

## Habitat and Mating Technique

Common near water, these spiders are found in swamps, reed-beds or boggy woodlands. They habitually weave their horizontal wheel-like webs overhanging water. With their long legs, they can comfortably straddle across the strands of their distinctively flimsy, sparse webs even though they are very far apart. During the day these spiders find a twig or reed-stem near the web and, extending their legs fore and aft to form one long slender line, they huddle motionless against it, making them extremely difficult to find.

The distinctive jaws are used in mating. The male has a forward-curving spine on each of his chelicerae which is situated so that when he meets a mate head-to-head his spines interlock with her jaws in such a manner that they are forced open and she cannot bite him. Similarly, his exceptionally long pedipalps enable him to impregnate her 'at arm's length'.

# Tent-web Spiders

*The tent-web spiders are named for the peaked struc-
ture of their horizontal webs.*

*T*ent-web spiders are orb-weavers and
they do indeed build orb-shaped
webs but the structure is difficult to grasp
visually because the webs are usually
horizontal, exceptionally closely woven
and often entangled with neighbouring
webs. The whole structure is supported from above by numerous vertical
threads, including one or more that pulls the whole web up sharply at its
centre, giving it a roughly tent-shaped appearance. Like those of the golden
orb-weavers, these webs are more or less
permanent, being repaired or replaced only
when necessary. In summer they are dotted with
the small, oval, papery egg-sacs, which in most
species are pale greenish blue in colour.

## Appearance and Distribution
The group is widespread and comprises several
species. There is a trend towards smaller, more
solitary forms in the south and large, communal
forms in the tropics. One spectacular tropical
species is black and white in colour, nearly 2 cm
in body length and builds enormous communal
webs that may sprawl over an area four or five
metres across.

> **ABANDONING
> THE WEB**
> As a prey-catching device,
> it's not easy to imagine any-
> thing more hi-tech than
> the silken web used by the
> orb-web weaving spiders, yet
> — for unknown reasons —
> many of these spiders have
> long ago abandoned its use
> and evolved even cleverer
> ways of ways of using silk to
> catch prey.

# Golden Orb-weavers

*While the leg span of the female golden orb-weaver spiders may reach 9 cm, those of the tiny male are often less than 1cm.*

*A*ustralia has about eight species of these orb-weavers, which are also widespread from Africa to the Pacific. As their name suggests, golden orb-weavers are readily identified by the rich golden yellow colour of the silk used to build their webs. In addition to this distinctive colour, webs are almost identifiable on size alone. Always vertical or nearly so and typically slung between two tree trunks several metres apart at almost any height above two metres, they are among the largest webs built by any Australian spider.

Aside from size and colour, the webs also have several unusual structural features. As with most orb-web weaving spiders, these spiders normally construct a framework to serve as a sort of scaffolding from which to build the sticky spiral but, unlike most, they leave it standing. Also, the web is seldom exactly symmetrical: the hub is usually noticeably higher than its geometrical centre. The separate webs of golden orb-weavers are often so abundant, especially in early autumn, that they nearly touch one another.

## Size and Appearance

The females of most golden orb-weavers are handsome spiders and some species are very large, with bodies up to 4 cm or so in length and legs spanning 9 cm or more. They have creamy grey bodies, brightly patterned in some tropical species, and legs that are conspicuously banded with black and yellow. Males are similar but considerably smaller; it often takes careful searching to find one or several lurking inconspicuously at the outer margins of the web.

# St Andrew's Cross Spiders

*The* 25 different species in this group are easily recognised by their distinctive webs, on which two broad ribbons form an X-shaped cross. At the centre the spider often mimics the 'X' effect by holding each pair of legs outstretched and almost straight along the four 'arms' of the cross. As youngsters, these spiders weave a roughly circular disc of silk at the web's centre as a sort of foundation for the cross but mature spiders normally dispense with the disc.

## Appearance, Behaviour and Mating

The oval abdomens are often conspicuously marked with bands or spots of black, yellow and sometimes red. Although appearing dissimilar, they are closely related to garden spiders and resemble much of their behaviour. Webs are permanent and females remain at their centre both day and night, dropping promptly to the ground only if alarmed.

*The distinctive X-shaped cross in the web of a St Andrew's cross spider is easily seen.*

Far smaller than the females, courting males loiter inconspicuously on the web's outer margins, often on the opposite side to the female. Mating is a precarious adventure for him; she often attacks him and he may shed a leg to distract her, falling to the ground to escape.

---

### MYSTERY THREADS

Some spiders, such as St Andrew's Cross spiders, incorporate a band of zigzag or 'fluffed-up' silk into their webs. Known as a stabilimentum, the function of the band is uncertain. It may lend stability but another plausible, although unproven, idea is that it is there to warn flying birds against accidentally flying into the web and in so doing confronting the spider with a costly reconstruction job.

---

# How do Spiders Grow?

*A huntsman spider in the midst of the intricate and dangerous process of moulting, when it is most vulnerable.*

Spiders, like lobsters and insects, have bodies encased in a nearly rigid outer skin, called an exoskeleton. This means that gradual growth is impossible. The only way for such an animal to grow bigger is to first moult or shed its skin. The moulting process is always a time of grave risk for a spider because it is extraordinarily intricate and there is much to go wrong, and also because the animal is virtually helpless while it is happening.

## Moulting Step-by-step

In the essential steps of moulting, a new skin is first prepared below the old and various proteins and minerals are extracted from the outer shell. The shell then splits and the spider slowly wriggles free, one jointed leg at a time. Fluids are pumped below the new skin to expand it to its maximum size before it hardens; this may take several hours. The spider then resumes normal activities one size bigger than it was before. Most spiders moult only as often as is necessary to reach sexual maturity and then they stop growing. A large spider may moult as many as 10 times. Often the first moult takes place in the egg-sac; indeed part of its function is to provide as secure an environment as possible for this process.

*Immediately after a moult, spiders like this funnel-web often look especially 'new' and glossy.*

# Can Spiders Shed their Legs?

*A seven-legged spider is nearly as nimble as an eight-legged spider — and if the spider is very young a missing limb can be regenerated.*

Spiders can shed legs in much the same way as some lizards can shed their tails. If a predator grabs a leg, it can be shed by fracture at a special soft zone near the body where bleeding is quickly staunched. The leg is left twitching to distract the predator, the spider makes its escape and, having seven legs still, it is probably little inconvenienced. If a predator tears the leg off at some other point, the spider is likely to bite off the stump at the fracture zone as a way of stopping the bleeding.

# Up, up and Away…

Many spiders disperse using a method known as ballooning. Soon after hatching, baby spiders crawl to the highest point they can conveniently reach, possibly the tip of a blade of grass or the top of a fence-post. From here the baby spider turns to face into the wind and, standing on tiptoe, it curves its body upwards and begins to reel out a single gossamer strand of silk from its spinnerets. Acting as a sort of miniature kite, this thread is soon long enough — 10–20 cm or so — to support the spiderling's minute weight, at which point it lets go to be carried off on the wind. Depending on the weather conditions, such 'balloonists' may be lifted to great heights and are sometimes carried hundreds or even thousands of kilometres from their birthplace.

*Soon these baby spiders will disperse, wafted kite-like on the breeze dangling from a silken thread.*

# Spiny Spiders

*The spiny spiders look very much like prickly crab spiders but these spiders are web-builders.*

In their bright colours and bold patterns, spiny spiders might almost be mistaken for crab or flower spiders but they differ most obviously not in their appearance but in the fact that they build webs. Among the most accomplished of the web-weavers, they construct large, vertical and strongly symmetrical webs. These have 20 or 30 spokes radiating outward from a central hub and a spiral-catching thread. Distinctive features of their webs are the small, fluffy balls of silk often scattered over the surface and the long dangling strands of silk, threaded with bundled insect remains and sometimes leaf debris.

They are well named spiny spiders as they bear up to six sharp spines on their abdomens. Depending on the species, these may be short and stout or extremely long and slender; the function of such striking adornments is unknown. Spiny spiders are compact and short-legged, with a very broad, heavily armoured abdomen. In some species the abdomen is black and liberally spotted with bright yellow but others show a variety of patterns and colours.

## Habitat and Behaviour

Spiny spiders vary widely in abundance and their habitat requirements are not well understood but they seem to be most common in shrubby thickets in gullys, swampy ground or along the banks of creeks. Most of them are solitary but at least one well-known species, the Christmas Spider, is social and builds large communal webs that may be shared by hundreds or sometimes even thousands of individual spiders.

# Wrap-around Spiders

*A wrap-around spider uses its extraordinarily flattened body to blend into the bark of a tree-branch.*

The wrap-around spiders are so named from their extraordinary broad, flat, or even concave, abdomens. These are triangular or heart-shaped and curved in such a way that when the spider is resting on a twig or similar substrate the abdomen moulds itself to suit the surface of the perch. The result looks very like a node or knobbly bit of twig. This 'shape' camouflage is extraordinarily effective and wrap-around spiders take a great deal of patience to find while they are resting during the day, although they are by no means uncommon. Occasionally they can be found dangling from a twig at the end of a short length of silk.

## Description, Prey and Egg-sacs

Most species are small, 1.5 cm or so in body length, but a few are substantially larger. Males and females usually differ little in size. The upper surface of the abdomen is knobbly, dimpled and covered with short hairs, and in some species carries a long blunt spike or turret that reinforces its resemblance to a twig. In some species the underside of the abdomen is black and shiny.

Common colours are dull brown or grey but at least one species is dull green and among some species the abdomen is blotched with black in a pattern that somewhat resembles a leopard's spots. Wrap-around spiders build large, vertical webs in which they catch flying insects, especially moths, at night.

> **INCONSPICUOUS EGG-SACS**
> The egg-sacs of wrap-around spiders are nearly as well camouflaged as the adults themselves, being loosely woven in dull brown silk and attached inconspicuously to a twig or similar object.

# Do Spiders Mind their Eggs?

*Most spiders guard their eggs well and wolf spiders carry them about even while hunting.*

*O*ne of the less obvious but most distinctive of spider traits is the care that female spiders take over their eggs. On the whole, insects and similar creatures tend to lay their eggs and leave them but spiders go to more elaborate lengths to ensure the safety of their eggs.

As soon as they are laid, the spider almost invariably wraps the eggs in silk to form an egg-sac or cocoon. Many spiders wrap their egg-sac into a ball covered with loose, flocculent silk; depending on the species; the silk is often coloured in delicate pastel shades of blue-green, golden yellow, white or pink. Other spiders build spindle-shaped or flat, disk-like cocoons. Some spiders construct only one egg sac at a time but others, such as the crab spiders and net-casting spiders, build three or four, each containing about 60–100 eggs.

> **SPIDER EGGS**
> Spider eggs are small, shiny and spherical, and very rich in yolk. The number of eggs laid varies widely with species, from about 10–20 in some jumping spiders to about 200 or so in wolf spiders.

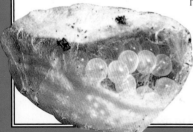

*The eggs within are easily visible in this close-up of a jumping spider's egg-sac.*

For the time it takes their eggs to hatch, many female spiders go without food. Some weave a special silken brood chamber or nursery and seal themselves in with their eggs. In a few cases, as in some jumping spiders, both male and female guard the eggs together. Others, such as huntsman spiders and wolf spiders, carry their egg-sacs with them wherever they go, even when hunting.

# What do Baby Spiders Look Like?

*U*nlike most insects and similar animals, baby spiders emerge from their egg looking very like miniature versions of adults, many having gone through at least one moult while still within the shell. Bolas spiders, in fact, are unique among all spiders in that males emerge from the egg as sexually mature adults. For the first few days baby spiders do not feed: their minute stomachs lack any connection with the outside world and they survive on the last of the food reserves remaining in the yolk.

*Baby spiders hatch from the egg looking like miniature versions of the adult and juvenile spiders.*

# What is a Tarantula?

*The Garden Wolf Spider is found in Australia and is unrelated to but commonly mistaken for a tarantula.*

> **THE WORLD'S SMALLEST SPIDER**
> The world's smallest spider has a body length of only about 0.5 mm. It belongs to a group known only from the leaf litter of tropical rainforests. The whole group remained undiscovered until the 1980s and almost nothing is known of their biology.

*S*everal spiders are commonly referred to as tarantulas, both in Australia and North America, but the true tarantula is a large species of wolf spider found in southern Europe. Its name is derived from Taranto, a town in southern Italy where it was originally found. A bite from this species is often fatal and in Italy, sometime in the fifteenth century, a myth somehow arose that frenzied dancing would counteract the poison of the Tarantula and cure the victim. Such is the origin of the tarantella, an old Italian folk dance.

# Two-spined Spiders

*Two-spined spiders can be identified by the two long spines of their broad, colourful abdomens.*

Two-spined spiders are bright and colourful and they are easily mistaken for spiny spiders (see page 84). Their very broad, shiny abdomens are boldly patterned in vivid hues of deep red, yellow, white and black. They get their name from the two short, sharp, broadly conical spines towards the rear of the upper abdomen; these feel soft and almost rubbery to the touch. A most unusual feature of these spiders is their ability to change the colour of their abdomen; this function is controlled by the flow of various body fluids beneath their translucent skin.

## Habits and Mating

These web-weavers are small and are entirely harmless to humans. They are solitary and build their webs low, barely a metre or so from the ground. Two-spined spiders are unusual web-weavers in that they build no preliminary scaffolding of any kind during web construction. Their webs are designed to catch insects at night. By day they leave them and huddle, hidden and motionless, on the under-surface of leaves or in some similarly secure refuge.

Male two-spined spiders build no webs at all. On reaching sexual maturity, which they attain a little earlier than females, they promptly go in search of a female. They seek to approach her just as she is in the last stages of her final moult from the immature to adult state and mate with her while she is still recovering from the ordeal.

# Net Spiders

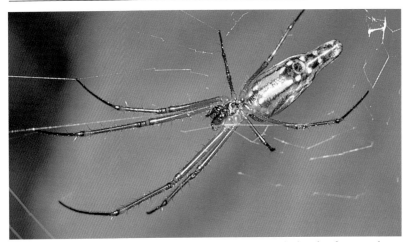

*A magnifying glass is needed to see the long slender hairs on the hindlimbs that identify a net spider.*

Not all web-weavers build conspicuous webs; there are hundreds of species that build small, unobtrusive webs in the grass, including many that are common and widespread. They include, for example, several small, attractive species belonging to the group *Leucauge* – there is no English name. About 1 cm long, these spiders can be identified, on close inspection, by a row of long, curved, slender hairs along the rearward margin of their fourth pair of legs. Their bodies are beautifully coloured in black, greenish yellow and silver, and their legs are pale green.

## Inconspicuous Webs

The net spiders build webs that resemble those of the more obvious web-weaving spiders except that they are very much smaller, horizontal rather than vertical and built close to the ground, partly hidden among blades of grass. The webs are often so inconspicuous that it is only in the very early morning, when a rising sun highlights the dew-spangled strands, that it becomes apparent just how abundant these small spiders are.

A hole at the hub of the web often leads to a daytime shelter of woven silk, or is sometimes pinned by silken cables to the ground below, forming a dip in the middle — the web then resembles a very shallow cone rather than a perfectly flat disk.

> ### SCORPION SPIDERS
>
> The scorpion spiders are three widespread species of Australian web-weavers that carry a cluster of four long spines at the tip of their abdomen. At rest, they often curve these spines well forward over their bodies in the way scorpions carry their tails.

# Leaf-curling Spiders

*A*bundant and widespread in Australian woodlands, leaf-curling spiders are easily recognised by their habit of incorporating a tightly curled leaf into their webs, usually near the top or off to one side. The web is roughly fan-shaped and its structure generally looks hasty and incomplete, with support strands laid at random. Usually situated within a few metres of the ground, the web is left standing during the day but normally rebuilt every night.

*Leaf-curling spiders are long-legged and plump-bodied but they hide by day in their curled-leaf lairs.*

The leaf chosen by the spider to be curled is hauled up on a silken thread from the ground, secured to the web with silk, and its opposite sides are brought together to form a rough tube. The result is a snug retreat in which the spider hides through the day with only the tips of its front pair of legs showing. Inside the leaf the spider is sheltered from sun and rain, and hidden from predators.

## Appearance, Courting and Nursery Construction

Reluctant to emerge, the spider itself is difficult to see. About 1.4 cm in body length, it is very sparsely haired and the legs are long and slender. Body and legs are mainly red-brown but the plump, egg-shaped abdomen is intricately dotted and marbled with white and grey.

Much smaller than the female, a courting male signals his approach to the female by tugging rhythmically at her web. If she rushes out to attack him he drops promptly to the ground and tries again later. After mating, males die and the female converts her curled-leaf shelter into a nursery for her eggs or she may construct a separate shelter off to one side of the web.

# Garden Spiders

*Garden spiders may be the best known of Australian spiders, common in almost any bushy backyard.*

The familiar vertical orb webs we see in gardens and parks are built by garden spiders. It is easy to blunder into these at night because they are often at about face height. Normally these webs are taken down and rebuilt nightly and the spider hides in nearby foliage during the day. As with other spiders that disassemble their webs, the silk is eaten.

There are a hundred or more species of garden spiders. Some are large — and a few rival the golden orb-weavers in the size of their webs — but most species are small or moderate in size. Most are compact spiders with very fat, rounded abdomens and rather short legs. There are few obvious peculiarities of shape or colour but a number of species have bright red markings on their legs.

> **CARTWHEEL GETAWAY**
> In the Namib Desert of southern Africa a spider known locally as the White Lady has evolved a unique escape technique. When alarmed this sand dune dweller partly folds its legs and cartwheels sideways down the steep face of the dune like a runaway bicycle wheel.

## Size Equality and Harmonious Mating

Unlike many web-weavers, the male is a similar size to the female with somewhat longer legs and a more slender body. Courting pairs build a dangling 'courtship' thread on which mating takes place. They hang suspended face to face, head down, alternately stroking each other's bodies with their front pairs of legs. Mating may take half an hour or more. Females do not carry their egg-sacs about, instead they hide them in nearby foliage or in their daytime retreat.

# Spotlighting Spiders

*Y*ou can watch a great deal of spider behaviour at night with nothing more elaborate in the way of equipment than a good torch or flashlight. By torchlight you can easily watch a spider building its web: usually the spider does not even seem to notice the intrusion and merely carries on, seemingly completely absorbed in its elaborate construction work. It is also possible to watch many roving spiders, such as wolf spiders, hunting at night. Their eyes shine in the torch's beam like those of minute cats or possums. As with larger animals, the trick in spotlighting spiders is to hold the torch close to your eyes so that your line of vision is as close to following the beam of light as possible.

# Photographing Spiders

*P*hotographing spiders is not difficult and you need go no further than your garden for suitable subjects. However, you need to select your equipment with care. Cameras come in two basic models, called 'rangefinder' models and SLRs. Ordinarily the distinction does not matter much but it becomes crucial when photographing very small objects such as spiders.

SLR is the common acronym for 'single lens reflex' and these cameras are fitted with a small internal mirror which reflects the image coming through the lens into the eyepiece as you look through it. When you press the trigger, the mirror flips out of the way to expose the film behind it. This means that when you compose the picture in the viewfinder of an SLR, you are seeing exactly the image that will strike the film when you press the shutter. This is not true of a rangefinder camera, which can neither be aimed nor focused accurately enough to get good pictures of very small objects very close up.

*Many leaf-haunting spiders, such as this Red-and-black Spider, are easy to photograph with the right equipment and a lot of patience.*

*Small subjects such as this distinctively patterned Knobble Spider may require a macro lens.*

## Going Macro

Many camera lenses will not focus closely enough to be useful for work with spiders but models called 'macro' lenses are specially designed to overcome this problem. Medium telephoto lenses are also useful. It may seem paradoxical to use a telephoto lens for extremely close-up work but if you try it you will probably find that getting a large image without needing to crowd your subject gives you much more control and 'elbow-room' in which to work. You may find that a macro telephoto lens with a focal lens somewhere in the range 75–200 mm is ideal.

Getting a good exposure of a very small, very close spider is tricky, even in strong sunlight. You can use electronic flash and sophisticated modern cameras do all the necessary calculations automatically. If yours is a simpler model, you need to experiment a little. You may find a reflector useful in getting more light onto your subject: try experimenting in the garden with an ordinary umbrella lined with aluminium foil.

### HOW TO SEX A SPIDER

The gender of many spiders can be established by looking carefully at the shape, size and structure of their pedipalps: those of females are merely slender and jointed but those of males are more elaborate, usually with an obviously swollen, bulbous tip.

# Are Red-back Spiders Native to Australia?

*The Red-back Spider may have been accidentally introduced to Australia sometime after European settlement.*

*T*he Red-back Spider has relatives around the world that look very similar and are equally venomous, so the question naturally arises, are they perhaps all the same species? With the very latest techniques of 'genetic finger-printing' now so widely used in criminal investigations, it should be possible to resolve the matter decisively but the exercise apparently has not yet been carried out. Meanwhile, three factors shed some light on the question. Firstly, red-backs do not feature in Aboriginal lore, secondly they are abundant around human habitation in Australia but very rare in the bush and finally, if red-backs are native and were as common at the time of European settlement as they are now in settled areas, it seems mysterious that it took 90 years to find one.

# Spiders as Pets

*A* large, hairy, bird-eating spider is not everybody's idea of the perfect house-hold pet, although it has been facetiously pointed out that logically there is little difference between such a spider and a kitten: the difference in size is not great, both are furry and both will inflict a painful nip if handled roughly. Spiders can make amiable pets but they are prone to exploitation: the Red-kneed Spider of Mexico's deserts, for example, is now an endangered species because of over-collecting for the North American pet trade. Many spiders can be easily maintained in captivity but any home has many perfectly wild spiders around about for the enthusiast to get acquainted with.

*Some spiders make good pets but cages are unnecessary. Given the run of the house, they will feed themselves.*

# A Checklist of Australian Spider Families

All the spiders mentioned in this book are listed under the three major groups, along with their scientific family name, which is included to help you if you want to look up the same spiders in other books.

**MYGALOMORPHAE**
**Ancient Spiders**
Trapdoor Spiders *Ctenizidae*
                 *Idiopidae*
Mouse Spiders *Actinopodidae*
Funnel-web Spiders *Hexathelidae*
Brush-footed Spiders *Barychelidae*
Bird-eating Spiders *Theraphosidae*

**HYPOCHILOMORPHAE**
Cave Spiders *Hickmaniidae*
            *Gradungulidae*

**ARANEOMORPHAE**
**Modern Spiders**
Sac Spiders *Clubionidae*
White-tailed Spider *Gnaphosidae*
Large Sac Spiders *Miturgidae*
Wolf Spiders *Lycosidae*
Huntsman Spiders *Heteropodidae*
                 *Selenopidae*
Badge Spiders *Heteropodidae*
             *Selenopidae*
Nursery-web Spiders *Pisauridae*
Net-casting Spiders *Deinopidae*
Two-tailed Spiders *Hersiliidae*
Spitting Spiders *Scytodidae*
Jumping Spiders *Salticidae*

Fiddle-back Spiders *Loxoscelidae*
Crab Spiders *Thomisidae*
Flower Spiders *Thomisidae*
Lace-web Spiders *Dictynidae*
                *Oecobiidae*
Lattice-web Spiders *Agelenidae*
                   *Stiphidiidae*
Daddy Long-legs *Pholcidae*
Gum-footed Spiders *Theridiidae*
Wheel-web Spiders *Uloboridae*
Long-jawed Spiders *Tetragnathidae*
Bolas Spiders *Araneidae*
Bird-dung Spiders *Araneidae*
Triangular Spiders *Araneidae*
Tent-web Spiders *Araneidae*
Golden Orb-web Spiders *Araneidae*
Garden Spiders *Araneidae*
St Andrew's Cross Spiders
              *Araneidae*
Spiny Spiders *Araneidae*
Wrap-around Spiders *Araneidae*
Two-spined Spiders *Araneidae*
Leaf-curling Spiders *Araneidae*

*There are about 2,000 different species of spiders in Australia.*

# INDEX